TUBE

SUBSTITUTION

HANDBOOK

by

The Howard W. Sams Engineering Staff

Howard W. Sams & Co., Inc.

4300 WEST 62ND ST. INDIANAPOLIS, INDIANA 46268 USA

Contents

Introduction

Although tube substitution should not be performed indiscriminately, there are numerous occasions when it is necessary and feasible. For example, when you don't have the exact tube type with you on a service call, you'll either have to take the chassis to the shop (without knowing if a new tube would fix the trouble), or else make a special trip just to get the tube. The same applies if you're working in the shop and need a replacement you don't have —you have to make a special trip to the distributor.

Also, when a tube is out of production or the distributor does not have it in stock, a substitute is needed. On occasion, too, it is desirable to use an improved version of the tube being replaced. For example, replacing a 6BK4 with the improved 6EN4 will usually result in better performance.

For your convenience, this handbook is divided into seven sections. The first section lists receiving tubes and their substitutes. The second section lists picture tubes and their substitutes. There are numerous occasions when a picture-tube substitute is necessary: The exact type may be out of production, or it may not be immediately available from the distributor; in either case it is necessary to use a substitute. Also, in custom installations a shorter-necked picture tube may have to be chosen. At the end of the picture-tube section is a listing of those tubes requiring odd filament voltages (other than 6.3 volts), or low E_{g2} potentials. This information can be very useful when setting up your picture tube testing and rejuvenating equipment.

Section 3 lists receiving tubes which can be replaced with industrial types. (Industrial tubes are more rugged than receiving types in that their peak ratings and power-handling characteristics are much higher; therefore, it may be desirable to substitute an industrial tube to get more satisfactory results.) Section 4 lists communications and special-purpose tubes.

Sections 5 and 6 list American and foreign equivalents. If you have an American tube and want to know what foreign type will serve as a substitute, refer to Section 5. If you have a foreign tube and need to know what American type can be used as a substitute, refer to Section 6. (Additional substitutes may be obtained by cross-referencing the American substitutes given in Section 6 with listings in Section 1.)

For additional information, refer to the introductions to each section. Also pay particular attention to the various notes pertaining to the substitutions.

The basing diagrams for tubes listed in Sections 1, 2, and 4 are given in Section 7. This section provides a handy reference to pin numbers for quick checks on a tube.

Cross Reference of American Receiving Tubes

This section lists all American receiving tubes which have been or are being manufactured. Also included are the latest tube types registered with EIA, but not yet in production.

To use this listing, locate in the left-hand column the tube type to be replaced. Then, refer to the right-hand column for the substitute. The substitutes are only those tubes which have similar, or improved, characteristics and can be inserted directly into the socket. No rewiring or mechanical changes are needed, although the associated service controls may have to be readjusted.

The x-radiation levels emitted from all television receivers produced after January 15, 1970 must meet rigid government standards. These radiations are primarily produced by high-voltage rectifier tubes, shunt-regulator tubes, and picture tubes. The radiation level is controlled in later designed tubes. In this tube substitution guide, wherever possible, only the newer tubes are suggested as replacements. While other substitutes may appear suitable, they have not been listed because of the possibility of excessive radiation which might occur.

In some instances, the available space around the tube should be considered. For example, although electrically identical to a 6L6GB, a 6L6G is more than one inch taller and a half inch larger in diameter. Thus, the substitution may be physically impossible in some compact equipment.

Do not replace a tube in the right-hand column with one in the left-hand column because this may result in a tube with lesser qualifications being used. For example, where a high heater-to-cathode potential exists, a 6AX4GTA will hold up, whereas a 6W4 will not. Thus, you'll find the 6AX4GTA listed as a substitute for the 6W4, but not vice versa.

When no substitutes are shown, none are recommended. Refer to Section 3 to see if an industrial replacement is recommended.

The Basing Code is given in the second column. Use this number and refer to Section 7 for the pin connections of the tube.

Tube Type	Basing	Replacement	Tube Type	Basing	Replacement
00A	4D		1AM4	6AR	1AF4, 1AJ4, 1T4SF,
01A	4D	12A, 112A			1AE4*, 1T4*
0A2	5BO		1AN5	7ES	
0A3	4AJ	0A3A, VR75	1AQ5	7AT	1R5SF, 1R5*
0A3A	4AJ	0A3, VR75	1AR5	6AU	1AF5, 1AH5, 1S5*
0A4G	4V		1AS5	6BW	1U5SF, 1DN5*, 1U5*
045	6CB		1AU2	9U	
0B2	5BO		1AU3	3C	1N2, 1N2A
0B3	4AJ	0B3A, VR90	1B3GT	3C	1AU3, 1G3GT,
0B3A	4AJ	0B3, VR90			1G3-GTA, 1G3GT/
0C2	5BO				1B3GT, 1J3, A,
0C3	4AJ	0C3A, VR105			1K3, A, 1N2, A
0C3A	4AJ	0C3, VR105	1B4	4M	1B4G, P, T, 951, 1A4,
0D3	4AJ	0D3A, VR150			P, T, 32, 34, 1C4*,
0D3A	4AJ	0D3, VR150			1K4*
0Y4	4BU	0Y4G	1B4G	4M	1B4, P, T, 951, 1A4,
0Y4G	4BU	0Y4			P, T, 32, 34, 1C4*,
0Z4	4R	0Z4A, 0Z4G (may			1K4*
		require shield)	1B4P	4M	1B4, G, T, 32, 951,
0Z4A	4R	0Z4, 0Z4G (may			1A4, P, T, 34,
		require shield)			1C4*, 1K4*
0Z4G	4R	0Z4, 0Z4A	1B4T	4K	1B4, G, T, 32, 951,
1A3	5AP				1A4, P, T, 34,
1A4	4K	1A4P, T, 1B4, G, P,			1C4*, 1K4*
		T, 951, 32, 34,	1B5	6M	1B5/25S, 25, 25S
		1C4*, 1K4*	1B5/25S	6M	1B5, 25, 25S
1A4P	4K	1A4, T, 1B4, G, P, T,	1B6	7AV	
		951, 32, 34,	1B7G	7Z	1B7GT, 1A7G*, GT*,
		1C4*, 1K4*			GT/G*, 1B7GT/G
1A4T	4K	1A4, P, 1B4, G, P, T,	1B7GT	7Z	1B7G, 1A7G*, GT*,
		951, 32, 34,			GT/G*, 1B7G/G
		1C4*, 1K4*	1B7GT/G	7Z	1B7G, GT, 1A7G*,
1A5G	6X	1A5GT, 1A5GT/G,			GT*, GT/G*
		1T5GT	1B8GT	8AJ	1D8GT§
1A5GT	6X	1A5G, 1A5GT/G,	1BC2	9RG	1BC2-A, 1BC2-B
		1T5GT	1BC2-A	9RG	1BC2-B
1A5GT/G	6X	1A5G, 1A5GT, 1T5GT	1BC2-B	9RG	
1A6	6L	1C6*	1BH2	9RG	1BH2-A
1A7G	7Z	1A7GT, 1B7G*, GT*	1BH2-A	9RG	
1A7GT	7Z	1A7G, 1B7G*, GT*	1BK2	9Y	1S2
1A7GT/G	7Z	1A7G, GT, 1B7G*, GT	1BX2	9Y	1X2-C
1AB5	5BF		1BY2	12HZ	1BY2-A
1AB6	7DH	1AC6*	1BY2-A	12HZ	
1AC6	7DH	1AB6*	1C4	4K	1K4, 1A4*, P*, T*,
1AD2	12GV	1AD2-A			1B4*, G*, P*, T*,
1AD2-A	12GY				32*, 34*, 951*
1AE4	6AR		1C5G	6X	1C5GT, GT/G, 1Q5G,
1AF4	6AR	1AJ4, 1AM4, 1T4SF,			GT, GT/G, 1T5GT*
		1AE4*, 1T4*, 1U4*	1C5GT	6X	1C5G, GT/G, 1Q5G,
1AF5	6AU	1AH5, 1AR5, 1S5*			GT, GT/G, 1T5GT*
1AH5	7DJ	1AF5, 1AR5, 1S5*	1C5GT/G	6X	1C5G, GT, 1Q5G, GT,
1AJ2	12EL				GT/G, 1T5GT*
1AJ4	7DP	1AF4, 1AM4, 1T4SF,	1C6	6L	1A6*
		1AE4*, 1T4*	1C7G	7Z	1D7G*

Tube Type	Basing	Replacement	Tube Type	Basing	Replacement
1D4G	5B	1D4GT	1G6GT	7AB	1G6G, GT/G
1D4GT	5B	1D4G	1G6GT/G	7AB	1G6G, GT
1D5G	5R	1D5GP, GT, 1E5G, GP, GT, 1K5G*, 1M5G*	1H2	9LX	
			1H4G	5S	1H4GT
1D5GP	5Y	1D5G, GT, 1E5G, GP, GT, 1K5G*, 1M5G*	1H4GT	5S	1H4G
			1H5	5Z	1H5G, GT, GT/G
1D5GT	5R	1D5G, GT, 1E5G, GP, GT, 1K5G*, 1M5G*	1H5G	5Z	1H5, GT, GT/G
			1H5GT	5Z	1H5, G, GT/G
			1H5GT/G	5Z	1H5, G, GT
1D7G	7Z	1C7G*	1H6G	7AA	1H6GT
1D8GT	8AJ	1B8GT§	1H6GT	7AA	1H6G
1DG3	8ND	1DG3-A	1J3	3C	1G3-GTA, 1K3-A
1DG3-A	8ND		1J3A	3C	1G3-GTA, 1K3-A
1DN5	6BW	1U5, 1AS5*, 1U5SF*	1J5G	6X	1J5GT, 1G5G, GT, GT/G
1DY4	7DK	1DY4A			
1DY4A	7DK	1DY4	1J5GT	6X	1J5G, 1G5G, GT, GT/G
1E3	9BG				
1E4G	5S	1E4GT, 1G4G, GT, GT/G	1J6G	7AB	1J6GT, GX
			1J6GT	7AB	1J6G, GX
1E4GT	5S	1E4G, 1G5G, GT, GT/G	1J6GX	7AB	1J6G, GT
			1K3	3C	1G3-GTA, 1K3-A
1E5G	5R	1E5GP, GT, 1D5G, GP, GT, 1K5G*, 1M5G*	1K3-A	3C	1G3-GTA
			1K4	4M	1C4, 1A4*, P*, T*, 1B4*, G*, P*, T*, 32*, 34*, 951*
1E5GP	5Y	1E5G, GT, 1D5G, GP, GT, 1K5G*, 1M5G*	1K5G	5Y	1M5G, 1D5G*, GP*, GT*, 1E5G*, GP*, GT*
1E5GT	5R	1E5G, GP, 1D5G, GP, GT, 1K5G*, 1M5G*			
1E7G	8C	1E7GT	1K7G	7AD	
1E7GT	8C	1E7G	1L4	6AR	1AE4*
1F4	5K		1L5G	6X	1F5G*
1F5G	6X	1L5G*	1L6	7DC	1U6*
1F6	6W		1LA4	5AD	1LA4E
1F7G	7AD	1F7GH, GT, GV, GY	1LA4E	5AD	1LA4
1F7GH	7AD	1F7G, GT, GV, GY	1LA6	7AK	1LC6
1F7GT	7AD	1F7G, GH, GV, GY	1LB4	5AD	
1F7GV	7AF	1F7G, GH, GT, GY	1LB6	8AX	
1F7GY	7AD	1F7G, GH, GT, GV	1LC5	7AO	1LN5
1G3GT	3C	1G3-GTA, 1K3-A	1LC6	7AK	1LA6
1G3-GTA	3C	1K3-A	1LD5	6AX	
1G3GT/1B3GT	3C	1G3-GTA, 1K3-A	1LE3	4AA	1LF3
1G4G	5S	1G4GT, GT/G, 1E4G, GT	1LF3	4AA	1LE3
			1LG5	7AO	
1G4GT	5S	1G4G, GT/G, 1E4G, GT	1LH4	5AG	
			1LN5	7AO	1LC5
1G4GT/G	5S	1G4G, GT, 1E4G, GT	1M3	8EM	1N3
1G5G	6X	1G5GT, GT/G, 1J5G, GT	1M5G	5Y	1K5G, 1D5G*, GP*, GT*, 1E5G*, GP*, GT*
1G5GT	6X	1G5G, GT/G, 1J5G, GT			
1G5GT/G	6X	1G5G, GT, 1J5G, GT	1N3	8EM	1M3
1G6G	7AB	1G6GT, GT/G	1N5G	5Y	1N5GT, GT/G, 1P5G, GT

§ May not work in all circuits.   * Parallel-filament circuits.
† Series circuit not requiring controlled warm-up time.

Tube Type	Basing	Replacement	Tube Type	Basing	Replacement
1N5GT	5Y	1N5G, 1N5GT/G, 1P5G, 1P5GT	2AH2	12DG	
			2AS2	12EW	2AS2A
1N5GT/G	5Y	1N5G, GT, 1P5G, GT	2AS2A	12EW	
1N6G	7AM	1N6GT	2AV2	9U	2BA2
1N6GT	7AM	1N6G	2AZ2	9Y	2BJ2A
1P5G	5Y	1P5GT, 1N5G, GT, GT/G	2B3	8HC	
			2B6	7J	
1P5GT	5Y	1P5G, 1N5G, GT, GT/G	2B7	7D	2B7S
			2B7S	7D	2B7
1Q5G	6AF	1Q5GT, GT/G, 1C5G, GT, GT/G, 1T5GT*	2BA2	9U	2AV2
			2BJ2	9RT	2BJ2A
1Q5GT	6AF	1Q5G, GT/G, 1C5G, GT, GT/G, 1T5GT*	2BJ2A	9RT	
			2BN4	7EG	2BN4A
1Q5GT/G	6AF	1Q5G, GT, 1C5G, GT, GT/G, 1T5GT*	2BN4A	7EG	2BN4
			2BU2	12JB	
1R4	4AH		2CN3A	8MU	2CN3B
1R5	7AT	1R5SF*, 1AQ5*	2CN3B	8MU	
1R5SF	7AT	1AQ5, 1R5*	2CQ3	8MK	
1S2A	9DT	1S2B	2CW4	12AQ	2DS4
1S2B	9DT		2CY5	7EW	2EA5, 2EV5
1S4	7AV		2DF4	9JL	
1S5	6AU	1AF5*, 1AH5*, 1AR5*	2DS4	12AQ	2CW4
1SA6GT	6BD		2DV4	12EA	
1SB6GT	6BE		2DX4	7DK	
1T4	6AR	1AE4*, 1AF4*, 1AJ4*, 1AM4*, 1T4SF*	2DY4	7DK	2DY4A
			2DY4A	7DK	2DY4
1T4SF	6AR	1AE4*, 1AF4, 1AJ4, 1AM4, 1T4*	2DZ4	7DK	2AF4B§
			2E5	6R	
1T5GT	6X	1A5G, GT, GT/G, 1C5*, GT*, GT/G*, 1Q5G*, GT/G*	2EA5	7EW	2EV5
			2EG4	12AQ	
			2EN5	7FL	
1U4	6AR	1AF4*	2ER5	7FN	2ES5, 2FQ5, 2FQ5A, 2FY5
1U5	6BW	1DN5, 1AS5*, 1U5SF*			
1U5SF	6BW	1AS5, 1DN5*, 1U5*	2ES5	7FN	2ER5*†
1U6	7DC	116*	2EV5	7EW	2EA5
1V	4G	6Z3	2FH5	7FP	2ES5, 2FQ5, 2FQ5A, 2GK5
1V2	9U				
1W4	5BZ		2FQ5	7FP	2FQ5A, 2ES5, 2FY5*†, 2GK5
1X2	9Y	1BX2, 1X2-C			
1X2A	9Y	1BX2, 1X2-C	2FQ5A	7FP	2FQ5, 2ES5, 2FY5*†, 2GK5
1X2B	9Y	1BX2, 1X2-C			
1X2-C	9Y	1BX2	2FS5	7GA	2GU5
1Y2	4P		2FV6	7FQ	
1Z2	7CB		2FY5	7FP	2ER5, 2FQ5, A, 2GK5
2A3	4D	2A3H	2G5	6R	
2A3H	4D	2A3	2GK5	7FP	2FQ5, A
2A5	6B		2GU5	7GA	2FS5
2A6	6G		2GW5	7GK	
2A7	7C	2A7S	2HA5	7GM	2HK5, 2HM5, 2HQ5
2A7S	7C	2A7	2HK5	7GM	2HM5, 2HQ5, 2HA5†
2AF4	7DK	2AF4A, B, 2DZ4§, 2T4§	2HM5	7GM	2HA5, 2HK5, 2HQ5
			2HQ5	7GM	2HA5, 2HK5, 2HM5
2AF4A	7DK	2AF4B, 2DZ4§, 2T4§	2HR8	9BJ	
2AF4B	7DK	2DZ4§	2J2	9DT	

Tube Type	Basing	Replacement	Tube Type	Basing	Replacement
2S/4S	5D	4S	3BF2	12GQ	
2T4	7DK	2AF4§, A§, B§, 2DZ4§	3BL2	12HK	3AT2B, 3BL2A, 3BM2A, 3BN2A
2V2	8FV	3C2	3BL2A	12HK	3AT2B, 3BM2A, 3BN2A
2V3G	4Y				
2W3	4X	2W3GT	3BM2	12HK	3AT2B, 3BL2A, 3BM2A
2W3GT	4X	2W3	3BM2A	12HK	3AT2B, 3BL2A
2X3G	4X		3BN2	12FV	3AT2B, 3BL2A, 3BM2A
2Y2	4AB	2X2, A	3BN2A	12FV	3AT2B, 3BL2A, 3BM2A
2Z2	4B	2Z2/G84, G84	3BN4	7EG	3BN4A
2Z2/G84	4B	2Z2, G84	3BN4A	7EG	3BN4
3A2	9DT	3A2A	3BN6	7DF	
3A2A	9DT		3BS2	12HY	3BS2B, 3BT2A, 3BW2
3A3	8EZ	3A3B, C, 3CU3A, 3CV3A, 3DB3, 3DJ3	3BS2A	12HY	3BS2B, 3BT2A, 3BW2
			3BS2B	12HY	3BT2A
3A3A	8EZ	3A3B, C, 3CU3A, 3CV3A, 3DB3, 3DJ3	3BT2	12HY	3BS2B, 3BT2A
			3BT2A	12HY	3BS2B, 3BW2
3A3B	8EZ	3A3C, 3CV3A, 3DB3, 3DJ3	3BU8	9FG	3BU8A, 3GS8, 3HS8, 3KF8
3A3C	8EZ	3DJ3	3BU8A	9FG	3BU8, 3GS8, 3HS8, 3KF8
3A4	7BB				
3A5	7BC		3BW2	12HY	3BS2B, 3BT2A
3A8G	8AS	3A8GT	3BX6	9AQ	3BY7
3A8GT	8AS	3A8G	3BY6	7CH	3BE6, 3CS6
3AF4A	7DK	3AF4B, 3DZ4§	3BY7	9AQ	3BX6
3AF4B	7DK	3DZ4§	3BZ6	7CM	3BA6§, 3CB6§, 3CE6§, 3CF6§, 3DK6§
3AJ8	9CA				
3AL5	6BT				
3AT2	12FV	3AT2A, 3BL2A, 3BM2A, 3BN2A	3C2	8FV	
			3C4	6BX	3E5, 3V4*
3AT2A	12FV	3AT2B	3C5GT	7AP	3B5, GT, 3Q5, G, GT, GT/G
3AT2B	12FV				
3AU6	7BK	3BA6, 3BC5§, 3CB6§, 3CE5§, 3CF6§	3C6	7BW	XXB
			3CA3	8MH	3CA3A
3AV6	7BT		3CA3A	8MH	
3AW2	12HA	3AW2A	3CB6	7CM	3CF6, 3DK6, 3AU6§, 3BC5§, 3BZ6§, 3CE5§
3AW2A	12HA				
3AW3	8EZ	3A3B, C, A, 3DB3, 3DJ3	3CE5	7BD	3BC5, 3AU6§, 3BZ6§, 3CB6§, 3CF6§, 3DK6§
3B2	8GH	3A3B, C, 3CV3A, 3CZ3A, 3DB3			
3B4	7CY		3CF6	7CM	3CB6, 3DK6, 3AU6§, 3BC5§, 3BZ6§, 3CE5§
3B5	7AP	3B5GT, 3C5GT, 3Q5, 3Q5G, GT, GT/G			
3B5GT	7AP	3B5, 3C5GT, 3Q5, G, GT, GT/G	3CN3	8MU	3CN3A, B
			3CN3A	8MU	3CN3, B
3B7	7BE		3CN3B	8MU	
3BA6	7BK	3AU6, 3BZ6§	3CS6	7CH	3BE6, 3BY6
3BC5	7BD	3CE5, 3AU6§, 3CB6§, 3CF6§, 3DK6§	3CU3	8MK	3A3C, 3CU3A, 3CV3A
			3CU3A	8MK	3A3C, 3CV3A
3BE6	7CH	3BY6, 3CS6	3CV3	8EZ	3A3C, 3CU3A,

§ May not work in all circuits.   * Parallel-filament circuits.
† Series circuit not requiring controlled warm-up time.

Tube Type	Basing	Replacement
		3CV3A, 3CZ3A, 3DB3, 3DJ3
3CV3A	8EZ	3A3C, 3CZ3A
3CX3	8MT	3DF3A
3CY3	8MX	3DB3, 3DJ3
3CY5	7EW	3EA5, 3EV5
3CZ3	8EZ	3A3C, 3CZ3A
3CZ3A	8EZ	3A3C
3D6	6BA	3LE4*, 3LF4*
3DA3	8MY	
3DB3	8MX	3DJ3
3DC3	8MZ	
3DF3	8MT	3DF3A
3DF3A	8MT	
3DG4	5DE	
3DH3	8NG	
3DJ3	8M8	3DB3
3DK6	7CM	3CB6, 3CF6, 3BC5§, 3BZ6§, 3CE5§
3DR3	8NL	
3DS3	8NL	3DR3
3DT6	7EN	3DT6A
3DT6A	7EN	3DT6
3DX4	7DK	
3DY4	7DK	3DY4A
3DY4A	7DK	3DY4
3DZ4	7DK	3AF4B§
3E5	6BX	3C4, 3V4*
3E6	7CJ	
3EA5	7EW	3EV5
3EH7	9AQ	3EJ7, 3HM6§, 3HT6§, 3JC6§, A§, 3JD6§
3EJ7	9AQ	3EH7, 3HM6§, 3HT6§, 3JC6§, A§, 3JD6§
3ER5	7FN	3FQ5, A, 3FY5
3ES5	7FN	
3EV5	7EW	3EA5
3FH5	7FP	3ES5, 3FQ5, 3FQ5A, 3GK5
3FQ5	7FP	3FQ5A, 3ES5, 3GK5
3FQ5A	7FP	3FQ5, 3GK5
3FS5	7GA	3GU5
3FY5	7FP	3ER5
3GK5	7FP	3FQ5, A
3GS8	9LW	3BU8, A, 3HS8, 3KF8
3GU5	7GA	3FS5
3GW5	7GK	
3HA5	7GM	3HK5, 3HM5, 3HQ5
3HK5	7GM	3HA5, 3HM5, 3HQ5
3HM5	7GM	3HA5, 3HK5, 3HQ5
3HM6	9PM	3HT6, 3JC6, A, 3JD6
3HQ5	7GM	3HA5, 3HK5, 3HM5
3HS8	9FG	3BU8, A, 3GS8, 3KF8
3HT6	9PM	3HM6, 3JC6, A, 3JD6
3JC6	9PM	3HM6, 3HT6, 3JC6A, 3JD6
3JC6A	9PM	3HM6, 3HT6, 3JC6, 3JD6
3JD6	9PM	3HM6, 3HT6, 3JC6, A
3KF8	9FG	3BU8, 3BU8A, 3GS8, 3HS8
3KT6	9PM	
3LE4	6BA	3LF4§, 3D6*
3LF4	6BA	3LE4§, 3D6*
3Q4	7BA	3S4§, 3S4SF*§, 3W4*§, 3Z4*§
3Q5	7AP	3Q5G, GT, GT/G, 3B5, GT, 3C5GT
3Q5G	7AP	3Q5, GT, GT/G, 3B5, GT, 3C5GT
3Q5GT	7AP	3Q5, G, GT/G, 3B5, GT, 3C5GT
3Q5GT/G	7AP	3Q5, G, GT, 3B5, GT, 3C5GT
3S4	7BA	3S4SF*, 3Q4§, 3W4*, 3Z4*
3S4SF	7BA	3W4, 3Z4, 3S4*, 3Q4*§
3V4	6BX	3C4*, 3E5*
3W4	7BA	3S4SF, 3Z4, 3S4*, 3Q4*§
3Z4	7BA	3S4SF, 3W4, 3S4*, 3Q4*§
4A6	8L	4A6G
4A6G	8L	4A6
4AU6	7BK	4BA6, 4BC5§, 4BZ6§, 4CB6§, 4CE5§, 4DE6§, 4CF6§
4AV6	7BT	
4BA6	7BK	4AU6, 4BZ6§
4BC5	7BD	4CE5, 4AU6§, 4CB6§, 4DE6§, 4DK6§, 4CF6§
4BC8	9AJ	4BQ7A, 4BS8, 4BX8, 4BZ7, 4BZ8, 5BK7A
4BE6	7CH	4CS6
4BL8	9DC	5EA8, 5U8, 5CQ8§
4BN4	7EG	
4BN6	7DF	
4BQ7A	9AJ	4BC8, 4BS8, 4BX8, 4BZ7, 4BZ8, 5BK7A
4BS8	9AJ	4BC8, 4BQ7A, 4BX8, 4BZ7, 4BZ8, 5BK7A
4BU8	9FG	4GS8, 4HS8, 4KE8, 4MK8
4BX8	9AJ	4BC8, 4BQ7A, 4BS8, 4BZ7, 4BZ8, 5BK7A
4BZ6	7CM	4JH6, 4AU6§, 4BA6§,

Tube Type	Basing	Replacement
		4CB6§, 4DE6§, 4DK6§, 4CF6§
4BZ7	9AJ	4BC8, 4BQ7A, 4BS8, 4BX8, 4BZ8, 5BK7A
4BZ8	9AJ	4BC8, 4BQ7A, 4BS8, 4BX8, 4BZ7, 5BK7A
4CB6	7CM	4CF6, 4DE6, 4DK6, 4AU6§, 4BC5§, 4BZ6§, 4CE5§
4CE5	7BD	4BC5, 4AU6§, 4BZ6§, 4CB6§, 4DE6§, 4DK6§, 4CF6§
4CF6	7CM	4CB6, 4DK6, 4AU6§, 4BC5§, 4BZ6§, 4CE5§
4CM4	9KG	
4CS6	7CH	4BE6
4CX7	9FC	
4CY5	7EW	
4DE6	7CM	4CB6, 4DK6, 4AU6§, 4BC5§, 4BZ6§, 4CE5§
4DK6	7CM	4CB6, 4CF6, 4DE6, 4BC5§, 4BZ6§, 4CE5§
4DT6	7EN	4DT6A
4DT6A	7EN	4DT6
4EH7	9AQ	4EJ7, 4HM6§, 4HT6§, 4JC6§, 4JC6A§, 4JD6§
4EJ7	9AQ	4EH7, 4HM6§, 4HT6§, 4JC6§, 4JC6A§, 4JD6§
4ES8	9DE	4KN8
4EW6	7CM	4GM6
4FS7	9MP	4HG8
4GJ7	9QA	4GX7
4GK5	7FP	
4GM6	7CM	4EW6
4GS7	9GF	
4GS8	9LW	4BU8, 4HS8, 4KF8, 4MK8
4GW5	7GK	
4GX7	9QA	4GJ7
4GZ5	7CV	
4HA5	7GM	4HK5†, 4HM5, 4HQ5
4HA7	12FQ	
4HC7	12FR	
4HG8	9MP	
4HK5	7GM	4HA5, 4HM5, 4HQ5
4HM5	7GM	4HA5, 4HQ5, 4HK5†
4HM6	9PM	4HT6, 4JC6, 4JC6A, 4JD6
4HQ5	7GM	4HA5, 4HM5, 4HK5†
4HR8	9BJ	
4HS8	9FG	4BU8, 4GS8, 4KF8, 4MK8
4HT6	9PM	4HM6, 4JC6, A, 4JD6
4JC6	9PM	4HM6, 4HT6, 4JC6A, 4JD6
4JC6A	9PM	4HM6, 4HT6, 4JC6, 4JD6
4JD6	9PM	4HM6, 4HT6, 4JC6, A
4JH6	7CM	4BZ6
4JK6	7CM	4EW6, 4JL6
4JL6	7CM	4EW6, 4JK6
4JW8	9DC	5JW8
4KE8	9DC	
4KF8	9FG	4BU8, 4GS8, 4HS8, 4MK8
4KN8	9AJ	
4KT6	9PM	
4LJ8	9GF	
4LU6	7CM	
4MK8	9FG	4BU8, 4GS8, 4HS8, 4KF8
4S	5D	2S/4S
5A6	9L	
5AF4A	7DK	
5AM8	9CY	
5AN8	9DA	
5AQ5	7BZ	
5AR4	5DA	
5AS4	5T	5AS4A, 5DB4, 5U4GB, 5V3, A
5AS4A	5T	5AS4, 5DB4, 5U4GB, 5V3, A
5AS8	9DS	
5AT4	5L	
5AT8	9DW	5BE8§, 5BR8§, 5CG8§, 5CL8§, A§, 5DH8§, 5FG7§, 5FV8§
5AU4	5T	5V3, A
5AV8	9DZ	5BB8§
5AW4	5T	5AS4, A, 5AU4, 5DB4, 5R4G, GTY, GY, GYA, GYB, 5U4GA, GB, 5V3, 5V3A
5AX4GT	5T	5AR4, 5AS4, A, 5R4G, GTY, GY, GYA, GYB, 5T4,

§ May not work in all circuits.   * Parallel-filament circuits.
† Series circuit not requiring controlled warm-up time.

Tube Type	Basing	Replacement	Tube Type	Basing	Replacement
		5U4G, GA, GB, / 5V4G, GA, GY	5GS7	9GF	5LJ8§
5AZ3	12BR		5GX6	7EN	5HZ6
5AZ4	5T		5GX7	9QA	5GJ7
5B8	9EC	5AV8§	5HA7	12FQ	
5BC3	9NT	5BC3A	5HB7	9QA	
5BC3A	9NT	5BC3	5HC7	12FR	
5BE8	9EG	5BR8§, 5CL8§, / 5CL8A§, 5FG7§, / 5FV8§	5HG8	9MP	
			5HZ6	7EN	5GX6
			5J6	7BF	
5BK7A	9AJ	4BC8, 4BQ7A, 4BS8, / 4BX8, 4BZ7, 4BZ8	5JK6	7CM	5EW6, 5JL6§
5BQ7A	9AJ	5BS8, 5BZ7	5JL6	7CM	5EW6, 5JK6§
5BR8	9FA	5FV8, 5BE8§, 5CL8§, / 5CL8A§	5JW8	9DC	4JW8
			5KD8	9AE	
5BS8	9AJ	5BQ7A, 5BZ7	5KE8	9DC	
5BT8	9FE		5KZ8	9FZ	5CR8§
5BW8	9HK		5LJ8	9GF	5GS7†§
5BZ7	9AJ	5BQ7A, 5BS8	5MB8	9FA	
5CG4	5L	5AR4, 5V4G, GA, / GY, 5Z4, G, GT, / GT/G, 5Z4MG	5MQ8	9AE	5CQ8§, 5GH8§
			5R4G	5T	5R4GTY, GY, GYA, / GYB
5CG8	9GF	5FG7, 5AT8§, 5BE8§, / 5BR8§, 5CL8§, A§, / 5FV8§	5R4GTY	5T	5R4G, GY, GYA, GYB
			5R4GY	5T	5R4G, GTY, GYA, GYB
5CL8	9FX	5CL8A, 5BE8§, / 5BR8§, 5FV8§	5R4GYA	5T	5R4G, GTY, GY, GYB
			5R4GYB	5T	5R4G, GTY, GY, GYA
5CL8A	9FX	5CL8, 5BE8§, 5BR8§, / 5FV8§	5T4	5T	5AR4, 5R4G, GTY, / GY, GYA, GYB
5CM6	9CK		5T8	9E	
5CM8	9FZ	5CR8§	5U4G	5T	5U4GA, GB, 5AR4, / 5AS4, A, 5AU4, / 5DB4, 5R4G, GTY, / GY, GYA, GYB, / 5T4, 5V3, 5V3A
5CQ8	9GE	5EA8§, 5U8§, 5MQ8§			
5CR8	9GJ	5CM8§, 5KZ8§			
5CU4	8KD				
5CZ5	9HN		5U4GA	5T	5U4GB, 5AS4, A, / 5AU4, 5DB4, 5R4G, / GTY, GY, GYA, / GYB, 5V3, A
5DB4	5T	5AS4, A, 5U4GB			
5DH8	9EG	5BR8§, 5CL8§, A§, / 5FG7§, 5FV8§			
			5U4GB	5T	5AS4, A, 5AU4, 5DB4, / 5V3, A
5DJ4	8KS				
5DN4	8KS	5DN4	5U8	9AE	5EA8, 5GH8, A, / 5GQ8§
5EA8	9AE	5GH8, A, 5U8, 5GQ8§			
5EH8	9JG	5X8§	5V3	5T	5V3A, 5AU4
5ES8	9DE		5V3A	5T	
5EU8	9JF		5V4G	5L	5V4GA, GY, 5AR4
5EW6	7CM	5GM6	5V4GA	5L	5V4G, GY, 5AR4
5FG7	9GF	5BE8§, 5BR8§	5V4GY	5L	5V4G, GA, 5AR4
5FV8	9FA	5BR8, 5BE8§, 5CL8§, / 5CL8A§, 5DH8§	5V6GT	7S	
			5W4	5T	5W4G, GT, GT/G, / 5AR4, 5CG4, 5R4G, / GTY, GY, GYA, / GYB, 5T4, 5V4G, / GA, GY, 5Y3G, GA, / GT, GT/G, 5Z4, G, / GT, GT/G, MG
5GH8	9AE	5GH8A, 5EA8, 5U8, / 5GQ8§			
5GH8A	9AE	5EA8, 5GH8, 5GQ8§, / 5MQ8§			
5GJ7	9QA	5GX7			
5GM6	7CM	5EW6	5W4G	5T	5W4, GT, GT/G,

Tube Type	Basing	Replacement	Tube Type	Basing	Replacement
		5AR4, 5CG4, 5R4G, GTY, GY, GYA, GYB, 5T4, G, GA, GY, 5Y3G, GA, GT, GT/G, 5Z4, G, GT, GT/G, MG	5Y4G	5Q	5Y4GA, GT
			5Y4GA	5Q	5Y4G, GT
			5Y4GT	5Q	5Y4G, GA
			5Z3	4C	83
			5Z4	5L	5Z4G, GT, GT/G, MG, 5AR4, 5CG4, 5V4G, GA, GY
5W4GT	5T	5W4, G, GT/G, 5AR4, 5CG4, 5R4G, GTY, GY, GYA, GYB, 5T4, 5V4G, GA, GY, 5Y3G, GA, GT, GT/G, 5Z4, G, GT, GT/G, MG	5Z4G	5L	5Z4, GT, GT/G, MG, 5AR4, 5CG4, 5V4G, GA, GY
			5Z4GT	5L	5Z4, G, GT/G, MG, 5AR4, 5CG4, 5V4G, GA, GY
5W4GT/G	5T	5W4, G, GT, 5AR4, 5CG4, 5R4G, GTY, GY, GYA, GYB, 5T4, 5V4G, GA, GY, 5Y3G, GA, GT, GT/G, 5Z4, G, GT, GT/G, MG	5Z4GT/G	5L	5Z4, G, GT, MG, 5AR4, 5CG4, 5V4G, GA, GY
			5Z4MG	5L	5Z4, G, GT, GT/G, 5AR4, 5CG4, 5V4GA, GY
5X3	4C	13, 80, 83V, 88	6A3	4D	
5X4G	5Q	5X4GA	6A4	5B	6A4LA§
5X4GA	5Q	5X4G	6A4LA	5K	6A4§
5X8	9AK	5EH8§	6A5	6T	6A5G
5Y3G	5T	5Y3GA, GT, GT/G, 5AR4, 5AX4GT, 5CG4, 5R4G, GTY, GY, GYA, GYB, 5T4, 5V4, GA, GY, 5Z4, G, GT, GT/G, MG	6A5G	6T	6A5
			6A6	7B	6A6X
			6A6X	7B	6A6
			6A7	7C	6A7S
			6A7S	7C	6A7
			6A8	8A	6A8G, GT, GTX, MG, 6D8*, G*
5Y3GA	5T	5Y3G, GT, GT/G, 5AR4, 5AX4GT, 5CG4, 5R4G, GTY, GY, GYA, GYB, 5T4, 5V4, GA, GY, 5Z4, G, GT, GT/G, MG	6A8G	8A	6A8, GT, GTX, MG, 6D8*, G*
			6A8GT	8A	6A8, G, GTX, MG, 6D8*, G*
			6A8GTX	8A	6A8, G, GT, MG, 6D8*, G*
			6A8MG	8A	6A8, G, GT, GTX, 6D8*, G*
5Y3GT	5T	5Y3G, GA, GT/G, 5AR4, 5AX4GT, 5CG4, 5R4G, GTY, GY, GYA, GYB, 5T4, 5V4, GA, GY, 5Z4, G, GT, GT/G, MG	6AB4	5CE	
			6AB5	6R	6N5, G, 6AB5/6N5
			6AB5/6N5	6R	6AB5, 6N5, G
			6AB6G	7AU	6N6*, G*, MG*
			6AB7	8N	6AB7Y, 6AC7, A, Y, 6AJ7, 6SG7*§, GT*§, Y*§, 6SH7*§, GT*
5Y3GT/G	5T	5Y3G, GA, GT, 5AR4, 5AX4GT, 5CG4, 5R4G, GTY, GY, GYA, GYB, 5T4, 5V4G, GA, GY, 5Z4, G, GT, GT/G, MG	6AB7Y	8N	6AB7, 6AC7, A, Y, 6AJ7, 6SG7*§, GT*§, Y*§, 6SH7*§, GT*
			6AB8	9AT	
			6AB9	10N	

§ May not work in all circuits.   * Parallel-filament circuits.
† Series circuit not requiring controlled warm-up time.

Tube Type	Basing	Replacement
6AC5	6Q	6AC5G, GT, GT/G
6AC5G	6Q	6AC5, GT, GT/G
6AC5GT	6Q	6AC5, G, GT/G
6AC5GT/G	6Q	6AC5, G, GT
6AC6G	7W	6AC6GT
6AC6GT	7W	6AC6G
6AC7	8N	6AC7A, Y, 6AB7, Y, 6AJ7, 6SG7*§, GT*§, Y*§, 6SH7*§, GT*§
6AC7A	8N	6AC7, Y, 6AB7, Y, 6AJ7, 6SG7*§, GT*§, Y*§, 6SH7*§, GT*§
6AC7Y	8N	6AC7, A, 6AB7, Y, 6AJ7, 6SG7*§, GT*§, Y*§, 6SH7*§, GT*§
6AC9	12GN	
6AC10	12FE	6U10§
6AD5G	6Q	6AD5GT
6AD5GT	6Q	6AD5G
6AD6G	7AG	6AF6G, GT
6AD7G	8AY	
6AD8	9T	6DC8, 6N8
6AD10	12EZ	6AD10-A, 6T10§
6AD10-A	12EZ	
6AE5	6Q	6AE5G, GT, GT/G, 6AF5G
6AE5G	6Q	6AE5, GT, GT/G, 6AF5G
6AE5GT	6Q	6AE5, G, GT/G, 6AF5G
6AE5GT/G	6Q	6AE5, G, GT, 6AF5G
6AE6	7AH	6AE6G
6AE6G	7AH	6AE6
6AE7G	7AX	6AE7GT
6AE7GT	7AX	6AE7G
6AE8	8DU	
6AF3	9CB	6BR3, 6AL3*
6AF4	7DK	6AF4A, 6AN4§, 6T4§
6AF4A	7DK	6AF4, 6AN4§, 6DZ4§, 6T4§
6AF5G	6Q	6AE5, G, GT, GT/G
6AF6G	7AG	6AF6GT, 6AD6G
6AF6GT	7AG	6AF6G, 6AD6G
6AF7G	8AG	6CD7*
6AF10	12GX	
6AF11	12DP	6AS11, 6BD11
6AG5	7BD	6BC5, 6CE5, 6AK5*, 6AU6§, A§, 6AW6§, 6CB6§, A§, 6CF6§, 6DC6§,

Tube Type	Basing	Replacement
		6DE6§, 6CY5*§, 6EA5*§, 6EV5*§
6AG6G	7S	6M6G*
6AG7	8Y	6AG7Y, 6AK7
6AG7Y	8Y	6AG7, 6AK7
6AG9	12HE	6AL9
6AG10	12GT	
6AG11	12DA	
6AH4GT	8EL	
6AH5	6AP	6AH5G
6AH5G	6AP	6AH5
6AH6	7BK	6AH6V
6AH6V	7BK	6AH6
6AH7GT	8BE	
6AH9	12HJ	
6AJ4	9BX	6AM4§, 6CR4*§
6AJ5	7BD	
6AJ7	8N	6AB7, Y, 6AC7, A, Y, 6SG7*§, GT*§, Y*§, 6SH7*§, GT*§
6AJ8	9CA	
6AK5	7BD	6AG5*, 6BC5*, 6CE5*, 6CY5*§, 6EA5*§, 6EV5*§
6AK6	7BK	
6AK7	8Y	6AG7, Y
6AK8	9E	6T8, A
6AK9	12GZ	
6AK10	12FE	
6AL3	9CB	
6AL5	6BT	6EB5
6AL6	6AM	6AL6G
6AL6G	6AM	6AL6
6AL7	8CH	6AL7GT
6AL7GT	8CH	6AL7
6AL9	12HE	6AG9
6AL11	12BU	
6AM4	9BX	6AJ4§
6AM5	6CH	
6AM6	7DB	
6AM8	9CY	6AM8A, 6HJ8
6AM8A	9CY	6AM8*†, 6HJ8
6AN4	7DK	6AF4§, 6AF4A§, 6T4§
6AN5	7BD	
6AN6	7BJ	
6AN7	9Q	
6AN8	9DA	6AN8A
6AN8A	9DA	6AN8*†
6AQ4	7DT	
6AQ5	7BZ	6AQ5A, 6BM5, 6HG5
6AQ5A	7BZ	6HG5, 6AG5*†, 6BM5*†
6AQ6	7BT	6AT6*, 6AV6*, 6BK6*, 6BT6*

Tube Type	Basing	Replacement
6AQ7GT	8CK	
6AQ8	9DE	6DT8*
6AR5	6CC	
6AR6	6BQ	6AR6G
6AR6G	6BQ	6AR6
6AR7GT	7DE	
6AR8	9DP	
6AR11	12DM	
6AS4GT	4CG	6DM4, A, 6DQ4, 6DT4, 6CQ4*, 6DE4*
6AS5	7CV	6CA5*
6AS6	7CM	6DB6*
6AS7G	8BD	6AS7GA, GT, 6080
6AS7GA	8BD	6AS7G, GT, 6080
6AS7GT	8BD	6AS7G, GA, 6080
6AS8	9DS	
6AS11	12DP	6AF11, 6BD11
6AT6	7BT	6AV6, 6BK6, 6BT6, 6AQ6*
6AT8	9DW	6AT8A, 6BE8§, A§, 6BR8§, A§, 6CG8§, A§, 6CL8§, A§, 6FG7§, 6FV8§, A§
6AT8A	9DW	6AT8*†, 6BE8A§, 6BR8A§, 6CG8A§, 6CL8§, 6CL8A§, 6FG7§, 6FV8§, A§
6AU4GT	4CG	6AU4GTA, 6CQ4*, 6DA4A*, 6DE4*, 6DM4*, A*, 6DQ4*, 6DT4*
6AU4GTA	4CG	6DM4A*, 6DT4*
6AU5GT	6CK	6FW5, 6AV5GA*, GT*
6AU6	7BK	6AU6A, 6BA6, 7543, 6AW6§, 6AG5§, 6BC5§, 6CB6§, A§, 6CE5§, 6CF6§, 6DE6§, 6DK6§
6AU6A	7BK	6AU6*†, 7543*†, 6BA6*†, 6CB6A§, 6CE5§
6AU7	9A	7AU7, 6AX7§
6AU8	9DX	6AU8A, 6AW8, A, 6BA8, A, 6BH8, 6CX8*, 6EH8*§, 6X8*, A*
6AU8A	9DY	6AU8, 6AW8, A, 6BA8, A, 6BH8, 6CX8*, 6EH8*§, 6X8*, A*

Tube Type	Basing	Replacement
6AV4	5BS	6BX4*
6AV5GA	6CK	6AV5GT, 6FW5, 6AU5GT*
6AV5GT	6CK	6AV5GA, 6FW5, 6AU5GT*
6AV6	7BT	6AT6, 6BK6, 6BT6, 6AQ6*
6AV11	12BY	6K11§, 6Q11§
6AW6	7CM	6CB6, A, 6CF6, 6DC6, 6DE6, 6AG5§, 6AU6§, A§, 6BC5§, 6BH6*, 6CE5§
6AW7GT	8CQ	
6AW8	9DX	6AW8A, 6AU8, A, 6BA8, A, 6JV8, 6KS8, 6LF8, 6EB8*, 6EH8*§, 6X8*§, 6X8A*§
6AW8A	9DX	6AW8, 6AU8, A, 6BA8, A, 6JV8, 6KS8, 6LF8, 6EB8*, 6EH8*§, 6X8*§, 6X8A*§
6AX3	12BL	
6AX4GT	4CG	6AX4GTA, GTB, 6AS4GT, 6DA4, A, 6DM4, A, 6DQ4, 6DT4, 6AU4GT*, GTA*, 6CQ4*, 6DE4*
6AX4GTA	4CG	6AX4GTB, 6DA4, A, 6DM4, A, 6DQ4, 6DT4, 6AU4GT*, GTA*, 6CQ4*, 6DE4*
6AX4GTB	4CG	6DM4A, 6CQ4*, 6DA4A*†, 6DE4*, 6DM4*†, 6DQ4*†, 6DT4*†
6AX5GT	6S	
6AX6G	7Q	
6AX7	9A	6AU7§, 6GU7*, 7AU7§
6AX8	9AE	6EA8, 6GH8, A, 6LM8, 6U8, A, 6CQ8§, 6GJ8§
6AY3	9HP	6AY3A, B, 6BA3, 6BS3, A, 6CK3, 6CL3, 6DW4, A, B, 6BH3*, A*
6AY3A	9HP	6AY3, B, 6BA3, 6BS3, A, 6CK3, 6CL3,

§ May not work in all circuits.   * Parallel-filament circuits.
† Series circuit not requiring controlled warm-up time.

Tube Type	Basing	Replacement
		6DW4, A, B,
		6BH3*, A*
6AY3B	9HP	6AY3, A, 6BA3, 6BS3,
		A, 6CK3, 6CL3,
		6DW4, A, B,
		6BH3*, A*
6AY11	12DA	
6AZ8	9ED	
6B3	9BD	6V3*, A*
6B4G	5S	
6B5	6AS	
6B6	7V	6BG6, 6Q7, G, GT,
		MG, 6T7G*
6B6G	7V	6B6, 6Q7, G, GT,
		MG, 6T7G*
6B7	7D	6B7S
6B7S	7D	6B7
6B8	8E	6B8G, GT
6B8G	8E	6B8, GT
6B8GT	8E	6B8, G
6B10	12BF	
6BA3	9HP	6AY3, A, B, 6BS3, A,
		6CK3, 6CL3, 6DW4,
		A, B, 6BH3*, A*
6BA6	7BK	6AU6, A, 6BD6,
		6CG6, 7543, 6BZ6§
6BA7	8CT	
6BA8	9DX	6BA8A, 6AU8, A,
		6AW8, A, 6BH8
6BA8A	9DX	6BA8, 6AU8, A,
		6AW8, A, 6BH8
6BA11	12ER	
6BC4	9DR	
6BC5	7BD	6AG5, 6CE5, 6AK5*,
		6AU6§, A§,
		6AW6§, 6CB6§,
		A§, 6CF6§, 6DC6§,
		6DE6§, 6DK6§,
		6CY5*§, 6EA5*§,
		6EV5*§
6BC7	9AX	
6BC8	9AJ	6BQ7, A, 6BS8, 6BX8,
		6BZ7, 6BZ8, 6HK8,
		X155, 6BK7*, A*,
		B*
6BD4	8FU	6BD4A, 6BK4*§, A*§,
		B*§
6BD4A	8FU	6BK4*§, A*§, B*§
6BD5GT	6CK	6AU5GT*, 6AV5GA*,
		GT*, 6FW5*
6BD6	7BK	6BA6, 6CG6
6BD7	9Z	
6BD11	12DP	6AF11

Tube Type	Basing	Replacement
6BE3	12GA	6BE3A
6BE3A	12GA	6BE3
6BE6	7CH	6BY6, 6CS6
6BE7	9AA	
6BE8	9EG	6BE8A, 6BR8§, A§,
		6CL8§, A§, 6FG7§,
		6FV8§, A§
6BE8A	9EG	6BE8*†, 6BR8A§,
		6CL8§, A§, 6FG7§,
		6FV8§, A§
6BF5	7BZ	
6BF6	7BT	6BU6
6BF8	9NX	
6BF11	12EZ	
6BG6G	5BT	6BG6GA
6BG6GA	5BT	6BG6G
6BH3	9HP	6BH3A, 6DW4A*, B*,
		6CJ3*, 6CK3*,
		6CL3*
6BH3A	9HP	6BH3, 6DW4A*, B*,
		6CJ3*, 6CK3*,
		6CL3*
6BH5	9AZ	
6BH6	7CM	6AW6*, 6CB6*, A*,
		6CF6*, 6DC6*
6BH8	9DX	6AU8, A, 6AW8, A,
		6BA8, A
6BH11	12FP	
6BJ3	12BL	6AX3
6BJ5	6CH	
6BJ6	7CM	6BJ6A
6BJ6A	7CM	6BJ6
6BJ7	9AX	
6BJ8	9ER	6BN8§
6BK4	8GC	6BK4C, 6EL4, A, 6EN4
6BK4A	8GC	6BK4C, 6EL4, A, 6EN4
6BK4B	8GC	6BK4C, 6EL4, A, 6EN4
6BK4C	8GC	6EL4, A, 6EN4
6BK5	9BQ	
6BK6	7BT	6AT6, 6AV6, 6BT6,
		6AQ6*
6BK7	9AJ	6BK7A, B, 6BC8*,
		6BQ7*, A*, 6BS8*,
		6BX8*, 6BZ7*,
		6BZ8*, 6HK8*,
		X155*
6BK7A	9AJ	6BK7, B, 6BC8*,
		6BQ7*, A*, 6BS8*,
		6BX8*, 6BZ7*,
		6BZ8*, 6HK8*,
		X155*
6BK7B	9AJ	6BK7*, A*, 6BC8*,
		6BQ7*, A*, 6BS8*,
		6BX8*, 6BZ7*,

Tube Type	Basing	Replacement	Tube Type	Basing	Replacement
		6BZ8*, 6HK8*, X155*			6HK8, X155, 6BK7*, A*, B*
6BK8	9BJ		6BR3	9CB	6AL3*
6BK11	12BY	6K11§, 6Q11§	6BR5	9DB	6DA5
6BL4	8GB	6AU4GTA*, 6CQ4*, 6DM4A*, 6DT4*	6BR7	9BC	
6BL7GT	8BD	6BL7GTA, 6BX7GT, 6DN7	6BR8	9FA	6BR8A, 6FV8, A, 6JN8, 6BE8§, A§, 6CL8§, A§
6BL7GTA	8BD	6BL7GT, 6BX7GT, 6DN7	6BR8A	9FA	6FV8, A, 6JN8, 6BR8*†, 6BE8A§, 6CL8§, A§
6BL8	9DC	6LN8			
6BM5	7BZ	6AQ5, A, 6DL5*, 6DS5*	6BS3	9HP	6BS3A, 6CK3, 6CL3, 6DW4, A, B
6BM8	9EX		6BS3A	9HP	6BS3, 6CK3, 6CL3, 6DW4, A, B
6BN4	7EG	6BN4A			
6BN4A	7EG	6BN4	6BS5	9BK	
6BN5	9CR		6BS7	9BB	
6BN6	7DF	6KS6	6BS8	9AJ	6BC8, 6BQ7, A, 6BX8,
6BN7	9AJ				6BZ7, 6BZ8, 6HK8,
6BN8	9ER	6BJ8§			X155, 6BK7*, A*,
6BN11	12GF				B*
6BQ5	9CV	7189, 7189A	6BT4	8HA	
6BQ6G	6AM	6BQ6GA, GT, GTA,	6BT6	7BT	6AT6, 6AV6, 6BK6,
		GTB, GTB/6CU6,			6AQ6*
		6CU6, 6DQ6, A, B,	6BT8	9FE	
		6FH6, 6GW6	6BU5	8FP	
6BQ6GA	6AM	6BQ6G, GT, GTA,	6BU6	7BT	6BF6
		GTB, GTB/6CU6,	6BU8	9FG	6BU8A, 6GS8, 6HS8,
		6CU6, 6DQ6, A, B,			6KF8
		6FH6, 6GW6	6BU8A	9FG	6BU8, 6GS8, 6HS8,
6BQ6GT	6AM	6BQ6G, GA, GTA,			6KF8
		GTB, GTB/6CU6,	6BV7	9BU	
		6CU6, 6DQ6, A, B,	6BV8	9FJ	
		6FH6, 6GW6	6BV11	12HB	
6BQ6GTA	6AM	6BQ6G, GA, GT, GTB,	6BW3	12FX	6AX3, 6BE3, 6BE3A
		GTB/6CU6, 6CU6,	6BW4	9DJ	
		6DQ6, A, B, 6FH6,	6BW6	9AM	
		6GW6	6BW7	9AQ	6BX6, 6EL7, 6HM6§
6BQ6GTB	6AM	6BQ6GTB/6CU6,	6BW8	9HK	
		6CU6, 6DQ6, A, B,	6BW11	12HD	
		6FH6, 6GW6	6BX4	5BS	6AV4*
6BQ6GTB/			6BX6	9AQ	6BW7, 6BY7, 6EL7,
6CU6	6AM	6BQ6GTB, 6CU6,			6EC7*
		6DQ6, A, B, 6FH6,	6BX7GT	8BD	6BL7GT, GTA, 6DN7
		6GW6	6BX8	9AJ	6BC8, 6BQ7, A, 6BS8,
6BQ7	9AJ	6BQ7A, 6BC8, 6BS8,			6BZ7, 6BZ8, 6HK8,
		6BX8, 6BZ7, 6BZ8,			X155, 6BK7*, A*,
		6HK8, X155,			B*
		6BK7*, A*, B*	6BY5G	6CN	6BY5GA
6BQ7A	9AJ	6BQ7, 6BC8, 6BS8,	6BY5GA	6CN	6BY5G
		6BX8, 6BZ7, 6BZ8,	6BY6	7CH	6BE6, 6CS6
			6BY7	9AQ	6BX6, 6EC7*

§ May not work in all circuits.   * Parallel-filament circuits.
† Series circuit not requiring controlled warm-up time.

Tube Type	Basing	Replacement	Tube Type	Basing	Replacement
6BY8	9FN				6AU6A§, 6CE5§,
6BY11	12E2				6HS6*§
6BZ3	12FX	6BE3, A, 6CD3*,	6CD3	12FX	
		6CE3*	6CD6G	5BT	6CD6GA, 6DN6, 6EX6
6BZ6	7CM	6DC6, 6HQ6, 6JH6,	6CD6GA	5BT	6EX6
		6BA6§	6CD7	8EV	6AF7G*
6BZ7	9AJ	6BC8, 6BQ7, A,	6CE3	12GK	6CD3, 6DU3
		6BS8, 6BX8, 6BZ8,	6CE5	7BD	6AG5*†, 6AK5*,
		6HK8, X155, 6BK7*,			6AU6A§, 6BC5*†,
		A*, B*			6CB6A§, 6CY5*§,
6BZ8	9AJ	6BC8, 6BQ7, A, 6BS8,			6EA5*§, 6EV5*§,
		6BX8, 6BZ7, 6HK8,			6HS6*§
		X155, 6BK7*, A*,	6CF6	7CM	6AW6, 6CB6, A,
		B*			6DC6, 6DE6, 6DK6,
6C4	6BG				6AG5§, 6AU6§,
6C5	6Q	6C5G, GT, GT/G,			A§, 6BC5§, 6BH6*,
		MG, 6J5, G, GT,			6CE5§, 6HS6*§
		GT/G, GTX, GX,	6CG3	12HF	6CD3
		MG, 6L5G	6CG6	7BK	6BA6, 6BD6
6C5G	6Q	6C5, GT, GT/G, MG,	6CG7	9AJ	6FQ7
		6J5, G, GT, GT/G,	6CG8	9GF	6CG8A, 6FG7, 6AT8§,
		GTX, GX, MG, 6L5G			A§, 6BE8§, A§,
6C5GT	6Q	6C5, G, GT/G,			6BR8§, A§, 6FV8§,
		6C5MG, 6J5, G,			A§
		GT, GT/G, GTX,	6CG8A	9GF	6FG7, 6CG8*†,
		GX, MG, 6L5G			6AT8A§, 6BE8A§,
6C5GT/G	6Q	6C5, G, GT, MG, 6J5,			6BR8A§, 6FV8§,
		G, GT, GT/G, GTX,			A§
		GX, MG, 6L5G	6CH3	9SD	6CJ3
6C5MG	6Q	6C5, G, GT, GT/G,	6CH6	9BA	
		6J5, G, GT, GT/G,	6CH7	9FC	6CX7
		GTX, GX, MG,	6CH8	9FT	6CU8§
		6L5G	6CJ3	9SD	6CH3
6C6	6F	77, 57A*, 57AS*	6CJ5	8GW	
6C7	7G		6CJ6	9AS	6DR6
6C8G	8G	6F8G*§	6CK3	9HP	6CL3, 6DW4, A, B,
6C9	10F				6CH3*, 6CJ3*
6C10	12BQ	6K11§, 6Q11†§	6CK4	8JB	
6CA4	9M		6CK5	8GW	
6CA5	7CV	6EH5, 6AS5*	6CK6	9AR	
6CA7	8EP		6CL3	9HP	6CK3, 6DW4A, B,
6CA11	12HN				6CH3*, 6CJ3*
6CB5	8GD	6CB5A, 6CL5	6CL5	8GD	
6CB5A	8GD	6CL5	6CL6	9BV	
6CB6	7CM	6CB6A, 6AW6, 6CF6,	6CL8	9FX	6CL8A, 6BE8A§,
		6DC6, 6DE6, 6DK6,			6BR8A§, 6FV8§, A§
		6HQ6, 6AG5§,	6CL8A	9FX	6CL8, 6BE8A§,
		6AU6§, 6AU6A§,			6BR8A§, 6FV8§, A§
		6BC5§, 6CE5§,	6CM3	9HP	6DN3
		6BH6§, 6HS6*§	6CM4	9KG	
6CB6A	7CM	6CB6*†, 6CF6*†,	6CM5	8GT	
		6DC6*†, 6DE6*†,	6CM6	9CK	
		6DK6*†, 6HQ6*†,	6CM7	9ES	
			6CM8	9FZ	6CR8§, 6CS8§

Tube Type	Basing	Replacement	Tube Type	Basing	Replacement
6CN6	8EW		6DA4A	4CG	6DM4A, 6DQ4, 6DT4,
6CN7	9EN				6CQ4*, 6DE4*
6CQ4	4CG	6DT4*, 6DE4	6DA5	9DB	6BR5
6CQ6	7DR		6DA6	9AU	
6CQ8	9GE	6EA8§, 6U8A§	6DA7	9EF	
6CR4	9BX	6AJ4*§	6DB5	9GR	
6CR5	9HC		6DB6	7CM	6AS6*
6CR6	7EA		6DC6	7CM	6AW6, 6BZ6, 6CB6,
6CR8	9GJ	6CM8§, 6CS8§			A, 6CF6, 6DE6,
6CS5	9CK	6DW5, 6CM6*			6DK6, 6AG5§,
6CS6	7CH	6BE6, 6BY6			6AU6§, A§, 6BC5§,
6CS7	9EF	6DA7*			6BH6*, 6CE5§
6CS8	9FZ	6CM8§, 6CR8§	6DC8	9HE	6AD8, 6N8
6CT3	9RX		6DE4	4CG	6CQ4, 6DA4A*,
6CT7	8GX				6DM4*, A*,
6CU5	7CV	6AS5*			6DQ4*, 6DT4*
6CU6	6AM	6BQ6GTB/6CU6,	6DE6	7CM	6AW6, 6CB6, A,
		6BQ6GTB, 6DQ6,			6CF6, 6DC6, 6DK6,
		A, B, 6FH6, 6GW6			6HQ6, 6AG5§,
6CU7	8GY				6AU6§, A§, 6BC5§,
6CU8	9GM				6BH6*, 6CE5§
6CV7	8GZ		6DE7	9HF	6EW7
6CW4	12AQ	6DS4	6DG6GT	7S	6W6, GT, 6EF6*,
6CW5	9CV				6EY6*, 6EZ5*
6CW7	9DD	6FC7	6DG7	9BA	
6CX7	9FC	6CH7	6DJ8	9DE	6ES8, 6FW8*, 6KN8*
6CX8	9DX	6EB8, 6GN8, 6HF8,	6DK3	9SG	
		6JA8, 6JE8, 6AU8*,	6DK6	7CM	6CB6, A, 6CF6, 6DC6,
		A*, 6AW8*, A*,			6DE6, 6HQ6,
		6JV8*			6BC5§, 6CE5§,
6CY5	7EW	6EA5, 6EV5, 6AG5*§,			6HS6*§
		6AK5*§, 6BC5*§,	6DL3	9GD	
		6CE5*§, 6HS6*§	6DL4	9NY	
6CY7	9EF		6DL5	7DQ	6BM5*
6CZ5	9HN	6DW5*	6DL7	8EV	
6D5	6Q	6D5G, MG	6DM4	4CG	6DM4A, 6DA4A,
6D5G	6Q	6D5, MG			6DQ4, 6DT4,
6D5MG	6Q	6D5, 6D5G			6CQ4*, 6DE4*
6D6	6F	78, 58AS*	6DM4A	4CG	6DT4, 6CQ4*
6D7	7H		6DN3	9HP	6CM3
6D8	8A	6D8G, 6A8*, G*,	6DN6	5BT	6CD6G, GA, 6EX6
		GT*, GTX*, MG*	6DN7	8BD	
6D8G	8A	6D8, 6A8*, G*, GT*,	6DQ3	12HF	
		GTX*, MG*	6DQ3A	12HF	6DQ3A
6D10	12BQ	6AV11*§, 6C10§,	6DQ4	4CG	6DT4, 6CQ4*, 6DE4*
		6K11*§, 6Q11*§	6DQ5	8JC	
6DA4	4CG	6DA4A, 6AX4GTA,	6DQ6	6AM	6DQ6A, B, 6FH6,
		GTB, 6DM4, A,			6GW6
		6DQ4, 6DT4,	6DQ6A	6AM	6DQ6B, 6FH6, 6GW6
		6AU4GT*, GTA*,	6DQ6B	6AM	6GW6*†
		6CQ4*, 6DE4*	6DR4	6BG	
			6DR6	9AS	6CJ6

§ May not work in all circuits.   * Parallel-filament circuits.
† Series circuit not requiring controlled warm-up time.

Tube Type	Basing	Replacement
6DR7	9HF	6FD7, 6FR7
6DR8	9HE	
6DS4	12AQ	6CW4
6DS5	7BZ	6AQ5*, A*, 6BM5*
6DS8	9CA	
6DT3	12HF	
6DT4	4CG	
6DT5	9HN	6EM5*
6DT6	7EN	6DT6A
6DT6A	7EN	6DT6
6DT8	9AJ	
6DU3	12JK	
6DV4	12EA	
6DW4	9HP	6DW4A, B, 6CK3, 6CL3
6DW4A	9HP	6DW4, B, 6CK3, 6CL3
6DW4B	9HP	6DW4, A, 6CJ3, 6CK3, 6CL3
6DW5	9CK	
6DX4	7DK	6DY4*§, A*§
6DX8	9HX	
6DY4	7DK	6DY4A, 6DX4*§
6DY4A	7DK	6DY4, 6DX4*§
6DY5	9CV	6CW5*
6DY7	8JP	6DZ7§
6DZ4	7DK	6AF4§, 6AF4A§, 6T4§
6DZ7	8JP	6DY7§
6DZ8	9JE	6FY8*
6E5	6R	6G5§
6E6	7B	
6E7	7H	
6E8	8O	6E8G
6E8G	8O	6E8
6EA4	12FA	6EH4, A
6EA5	7EW	6EV5, 6AG5*§, 6AK5*§, 6BC5*§, 6CE5*§
6EA7	8BD	6GL7, 6EM7
6EA8	9AE	6CQ8§, 6GH8§, 6KD8§, 6MQ8*, 6U8A*
6EB5	6BT	6AL5
6EB8	9DX	6CX8, 6GN8, 6HF8, 6JA8, 6JE8, 6AU8*, 8A*, 6HZ8*, 6JV8*
6EC7	9AQ	6BX6*, 6BY7*
6EF4	12HC	6EJ4, 6EJ4A
6EF6	7S	6EY6*, 6EZ5*
6EH4	12FA	6EH4A
6EH4A	12FA	
6EH5	7CV	6CA5
6EH7	9AQ	6EJ7, 6HM6§, 6HT6§, 6JC6§, A§, 6JD6§

Tube Type	Basing	Replacement
6EH8	9JG	6AU8*§, A*§, 6AW8*§, A*§, 6X8A§
6EJ4	12HC	6EJ4A
6EJ4A	12HC	
6EJ7	9AQ	6EH7, 6HM6§, 6HT6§, 6JC6A§, 6JD6§
6EL4	8MW	6EL4A, 6EN4
6EL4A	8MW	6EN4
6EL7	9AQ	6BW7, 6BX6, 6HM6§
6EM5	9HN	
6EM7	8BD	6EA7, 6GL7
6EN4	8NJ	
6EQ7	9LQ	6KL8§
6ER5	7FN	6FY5*
6ES5	7FN	
6ES6	7EN	6ET6, 6FD6
6ES8	9DE	6DJ8, 6FW8*, 6KN8*
6ET6	7EN	6ES6, 6FD6
6ET7	9LT	
6EU7	9LS	
6EU8	9JF	
6EV5	7EW	6EA5, 6AG5*§, 6AK5*§, 6BC5*§, 6CE5*§
6EV7	9LP	
6EW6	7CM	6GM6, 6HS6*§
6EW7	9HF	
6EX6	5BT	6CD6GA
6EY6	7AC	6EZ5*
6EZ5	7AC	
6EZ8	9KA	
6F4	7BR	6L4
6F5	5M	6F5G, GT, MG
6F5G	5M	6F5, GT, MG
6F5GT	5M	6F5, G, MG
6F5MG	5M	6F5, G, GT
6F6	7S	6F6G, GT, GT/G, MG
6F6G	7S	6F6, GT, GT/G, MG
6F6GT	7S	6F6, G, GT/G, MG
6F6GT/G	7S	6F6, G, GT, MG
6F6MG	7S	6F6, G, GT, GT/G
6F7	7E	6F7S
6F7S	7E	6F7
6F8G	8G	6C8G*§
6FA7	9MR	
6FC7	9DD	6CW7
6FD6	7BK	6ES6, 6ET6
6FD7	9HF	6FR7
6FE5	8KB	
6FE8	9AJ	
6FG5	7GA	6HS6*§
6FG6	9GA	
6FG7	9GF	6BE8A§, 6BR8A§

Tube Type	Basing	Replacement
6FH5	7FP	6ES5, 6FQ5*, A*, 6GK5*
6FH6	6AM	6DQ6B, 6GW6
6FH8	9KP	
6FJ7	12BM	
6FM7	12EJ	
6FM8	9KR	
6FN5	8GD	
6FQ5	7FP	6FQ5A, 6GK5, 6ES5*
6FQ5A	7FP	6FQ5, 6GK5, 6ES5*
6FQ7	9LP	
6FR7	9HF	6FD7
6FS5	7GA	6FG5, 6GU5*
6FV6	7FQ	
6FV8	9FA	6FV8A, 6BE8A§, 6BR8*†, 6CL8§, 6CL8A§
6FV8A	9FA	6FV8, 6BR8A, 6BE8A, 6BR8*†, 6CL8§, 6CL8A§
6FW5	6CK	
6FW8	9AJ	6KN8, 6DJ8*, 6ES8*
6FY5	7FP	6ER5*
6FY7	12EO	
6FY8	9EX	
6G5	6R	6G5/6H5, 6H5, 6T5, 6U5/6G5, 6U5
6G5/6H5	6R	6G5, 6H5, 6U5, 6U5/6G5
6G6G	7S	6G6GT
6G6GT	7S	6G6G
6G11	12BU	
6GA7	12EB	
6GA8	9AJ	6CG7*
6GB5	9NH	
6GC5	9EU	
6GC6	8JX	
6GD7	9GF	6LJ8§
6GE5	12BJ	
6GE8	9LC	
6GF5	12BJ	6GE5
6GF7	9QD	6GF7A
6GF7A	9QD	6GF7
6GH8	9AE	6GH8A, 6EA8, 6U8A, 6AX8*†, 6CQ8§, 6GJ8*, 6LM8*†, 6U8*†, 6HL8*†, 6KE8*
6GH8A	9AE	6GH8, 6EA8, 6AX8*†, 6CQ8§, 6GJ8*, 6LM8*†, 6U8*†, 6HL8*†, 6KE8*

Tube Type	Basing	Replacement
6GJ5	9QK	6GJ5A
6GJ5A	9QK	6GJ5
6GJ7	9QA	
6GJ8	9AE	6AX8*, 6CQ8*§, 6EA8*, 6GH8*, A*, 6U8*, A*
6GK5	7FP	6FQ5, A
6GK6	9GK	
6GK7	9AQ	
6GL7	8BD	6EA7, 6EM7
6GM5	9MQ	
6GM6	7CM	6EW6, 6HQ6*, 6JH6*
6GM8	9DE	
6GN6	7FW	
6GN8	9DX	6CX8, 6EB8, 6HF8, 6JE8, 6AU8*, A*, 6AW8*, A*, 6HZ8*, 6JA8, 6JV8*, 6LF8*
6GQ7	9RB	6BC7§
6GS8	9LW	6BU8, 6BU8A, 6HS8, 6KF8
6GT5	9NZ	6GT5A
6GT5A	9NZ	6GT5
6GU5	7GA	6FS5*
6GU7	9LP	
6GV5	12DR	
6GV7	9KN	
6GV8	9LY	
6GW5	7GK	
6GW6	6AM	6DQ6B
6GW8	9LZ	
6GX6	7EN	6GY6, 6HZ6
6GX7	9QA	
6GY5	12DR	
6GY6	7EN	6GX6, 6HZ6
6GY8	9MB	
6GZ5	7CV	
6H4	5AF	6H4GT
6H4GT	5AF	6H4
6H5	6R	6G5, 6G5/6H5, 6T5, 6U5, 6U5/6G5
6H6	7Q	6H6G, GT, GT/G, MG
6H6G	7Q	6H6, GT, GT/G, MG
6H6GT	7Q	6H6, G, GT/G, MG
6H6GT/G	7Q	6H6, G, GT, MG
6H6MG	7Q	6H6, G, GT, GT/G
6H8G	8E	
6HA5	7GM	6HK5, 6HM5, 6HQ5
6HA6	9NW	
6HB5	12BJ	
6HB6	9NW	

§ May not work in all circuits.   * Parallel-filament circuits.
† Series circuit not requiring controlled warm-up time.

Tube Type	Basing	Replacement
6HB7	9QA	
6HC8	9EX	6BM8*
6HD5	12ES	
6HD7	9QA	
6HE5	12EY	6JB5, 6JC5
6HE7	12FS	
6HF5	12FB	
6HF8	9DX	6CX8, 6EB8, 6GN8, 6JA8, 6JE8, 6HZ8*, 6JV8*, 6LF8*
6HG5	7BZ	6AQ5A, 6AQ5*†
6HG8	9MP	
6HJ5	12FL	
6HJ7	9QA	
6HJ8	9CY	6AM8A, 6AM8*†
6HK5	7GM	6HA5, 6HM5, 6HQ5
6HK8	9DE	6BC8, 6BQ7A, 6BS8, 6BX8, 6BZ7, 6BZ8, X155, 6BK7*, A*, B*
6HL5	9QW	
6HL8	9AE	6BL8*, 6GH8*†, A*†
6HM5	7GM	6HA5, 6HK5, 6HQ5
6HM6	9PM	6HT6, 6JC6, 6JC6A, 6JD6
6HQ5	7GM	6HA5, 6HK5, 6HM5
6HQ6	7CM	6BZ6, 6CB6, 6SB6A, 6DE6, 6DK6, 6JK6, 6GM6*
6HR5	7BZ	
6HR6	7BK	
6HS5	12GY	6HV5, A
6HS6	7BK	6CB6*§, A*§, 6CE5*§, 6CF6*§, 6CY5*§, 6DK6*§, 6EW6*§, 6FG5*§
6HS8	9FG	6BU8, A, 6GS8, 6KF8, 6MK8, A
6HT6	9PM	6HM6, 6JC6, A, 6JD6
6HU6	9GA	
6HU8	9NJ	
6HV5	12GY	6HS5, 6HV5A
6HV5A	12GY	
6HW8	9NQ	
6HZ5	12GY	
6HZ6	7EN	6GX6, 6GY6
6HZ8	9DX	6EB8*, 6GN8*, 6HF8*, 6JE8*, 6JV8*, 6LF8*
6J4	7BQ	
6J5	6Q	6J5G, GT, GT/G, GTX, GX, MG, 6C5, G, GT/G, MG, 6L5G
6J5G	6Q	6J5, GT, GT/G, GTX, GX, MG, 6C5, G, GT, GT/G, MG, 6L5G
6J5GT	6Q	6J5, G, GT/G, GTX, GX, MG, 6C5, G, GT, GT/G, MG, 6L5G
6J5GT/G	6Q	6J5, G, GT, GTX, GX, MG, 6C5, G, GT, GT/G, MG, 6L5G
6J5GTX	6Q	6J5, G, GT, GT/G, GX, MG, 6C5, G, GT, GT/G, MG, 6L5G
6J5GX	6Q	6J5, G, GT, GT/G, GTX, MG, 6C5, G, GT, GT/G, MG, 6L5G
6J5MG	6Q	6J5, G, GT, GT/G, GTX, GX, 6C5, G, GT, GT/G, MG, 6L5G
6J6	7BF	6J6A
6J6A	7BF	6J6*†
6J7	7R	6J7G, GT, GTX, MG, 6W7G*
6J7G	7R	6J7, GT, GTX, MG, 6W7G*
6J7GT	7R	6J7, G, GTX, MG, 6W7G*
6J7GTX	7R	6J7, G, GT, MG, 6W7G*
6J7MG	7R	6J7, G, GT, GTX, 6W7G*
6J8G	8H	
6J9	10G	
6J10	12BT	6Z10
6J11	12BW	
6JA5	12EY	
6JA8	9DX	6CX8, 6EB8, 6GN8, 6HF8, 6JE8, 6JT8, 6HZ8*, 6JV8*, 6LF8*
6JB5	12EY	6JC5, 6HE5
6JB5	9QL	6JB6A
6JB6A	9QL	6JB6
6JB8	9AE	
6JC5	12EY	6JB5, 6HE5
6JC6	9PM	6HM6, 6HT6, 6JC6A, 6JD6
6JC6A	9PM	6HM6, 6HT6, 6JC6, 6JD6
6JC8	9PA	
6JD5	12GY	6HV5A

Tube Type	Basing	Replacement	Tube Type	Basing	Replacement
6JD6	9PM	6HM6, 6HT6, 6JC6, A	6K5GT	5U	6K5, G
6JE6	9QL	6JE6A, B, C	6K6	7S	6K6G, GT, GT/G, MG
6JE6A	9QL	6JE6B, 6JE6C	6K6G	7S	6K6, GT, GT/G, MG
6JE6B	9QL	6JE6C, 6LQ6, 6LZ6, 6ME6	6K6GT	7S	6K6, G, GT/G, MG
			6K6GT/G	7S	6K6, G, GT, MG
6JE6C	9QL	6JE6B, 6LQ6, 6LZ6, 6ME6, 6MJ6	6K6MG	7S	6K6, G, GT, GT/G
6JE8	9DX	6EB8, 6GN8, 6HF8, 6JA8, 6HZ8*, 6JV8*, 6LF8*	6K7	7R	6K7G, GT, GTX, MG, 6U7G
			6K7G	7R	6K7, GT, GTX, MG, 6U7G
6JF6	9QL	6JE6*, 6KM6, 6LQ6*	6K7GT	7R	6K7, G, GTX, MG, 6U7G
6JG5	9SF				
6JG6	9QU	6JG6A, 6JR6, 6KV6A	6K7GTX	7R	6K7, G, GT, MG, 6U7G
6JG6A	9QU	6JG6, 6JR6, 6KV6A			
6JH5	12JE	6JK5	6K7MG	7R	6K7, G, GT, GTX, 6U7G
6JH6	7CM	6BZ6, 6HQ6, 6GM6*			
6JH8	9DP		6K8	8K	6K8G, GT, GTX
6JK5	12JE	6JH5	6K8G	8K	6K8, GT, GTX
6JK6	7CM	6EW6, 6JL6	6K8GT	8K	6K8, G, GTX
6JK8	9AJ		6K8GTX	8K	6K8, G, GT
6JL6	7CM	6EW6, 6JK6	6K11	12BY	6Q11
6JL8	9DX		6KA8	9PV	
6JM6	12FJ	6JM6A	6KD6	12GW	
6JM6A	12FJ	6JM6	6KD8	9AE	6EA8, 6GH8, A, 6U8, A
6JN6	12FK	6JN6A			
6JN6A	12FK	6JN6	6KE6	12GM	
6JN8	9FA	6BR8A, 6FV8, A, 6BR8*†	6KE8	9DC	
			6KF8	9FG	6BU8, A, 6GS8, 6HS8
6JQ6	9RA		6KG6	9RJ	
6JR6	9QU	6JG6, A	6KL8	9LQ	6EQ7§
6JS6	12FY	6JS6A, B, C, 6KD6	6KM6	9QL	6JF6, 6LQ6*
6JS6A	12FY	6JS6, B, C, 6KD6	6KM8	9QG	
6JS6B	12FY	6JS6, A, C, 6LB6	6KN6	12GU	
6JS6C	12FY	6JS6B, 6LB6A	6KN8	9AJ	
6JT6	9QU	6JT6A, 6JG6*, A*	6KR8	9DX	6KR8A, 6JT8, 6KV8, 6LB8, 6LQ8, 6LY8
6JT6A	9QU	6JT6, 6JG6*, A*			
6JT8	9DX	6JA8, 6KR8, A, 6KV8, 6LB8, 6LQ8, 6LY8	6KR8A	9DX	6KR8, 6JT8, 6KV8, 6LB8, 6LQ8, 6LY8
6JU6	9QL		6KS6	7DF	6BN6
6JU8	9PQ	6JU8A	6KS8	9DX	6AU8, A, 6AW8,
6JU8A	9PQ	6JU8			6AW8A, 6JV8,
6JV8	9DX	6AW8, A, 6KS8, 6LF8, 6CX8*, 6EB8*, 6GN8*, 6HF8*, 6HZ8*, 6JA8*, 6JE8*			6LF8, 6CX8*, 6EB8*, 6GN8*, 6HF8*, 6HZ8*, 6JA8*, 6JE8*
			6KT6	9PM	
6JW6	9PU		6KT8	9QP	
6JW8	9DC	6LX8	6KU8	9LT	
6JZ6	12GD		6KV6	9QU	6KV6A
6JZ8	12DZ		6KV6A	9QU	
6K5	5U	6K5G, GT	6KV8	9DX	6JT8, 6KR8, A, 6LB8, 6LQ8, 6LY8
6K5G	5U	6K5, GT			

§ May not work in all circuits.   * Parallel-filament circuits.
† Series circuit not requiring controlled warm-up time.

Tube Type	Basing	Replacement	Tube Type	Basing	Replacement
6KY6	9GK		6LJ6	8MQ	6LJ6A
6KY8	9QT	6KY8A	6LJ6A	8MQ	
6KY8A	9QT	6KY8	6LJ8	9GF	6GD7§, 6MB8§
6KZ8	9FZ		6LM8	9AE	6AX8, 6GH8, 6GH8A,
6L4	7BR				6CQ8§, 6LM8A
6L5G	6Q	6C5, G, GT, GT/G,	6LM8A	9AE	6AX8, 6CQ8§, 6GH8,
		MG, 6J5, G, GT,			A
		GT/G, GTX, GX,	6LN8	9DC	6BL8*†
		MG	6LQ6	9QL	6JE6B, 6JE6C, 6LZ6,
6L6	7AC	6L6A, G, GA, GAY,			6ME6, 6MJ6
		GB, GC, GT, GX, Y,	6LQ8	9DX	6JT8, 6KR8, A, 6KV8,
		5881, 7581, 7581A			6LB8, 6LY8
6L6A	7AC	6L6, G, GA, GAY, GB,	6LR6	12FY	6JS6C
		GC, GT, GX, Y,	6LR8	9QT	
		5881, 7581, 7581A	6LT8	9RL	
6L6G	7AC	6L6, A, GA, GAY, GB,	6LU6	7CM	
		GC, GT, GX, Y,	6LU8	12DZ	6MY8
		5881, 7581, 7581A	6LV6	12GW	6LF6
6L6GA	7AC	6L6, A, G, GAY, GB,	6LW6	8NC	
		GC, GT, GX, Y,	6LX6	12JA	
		5881, 7581, 7581A	6LX8	9DC	6JW8*†
6L6GAY	7AC	6L6, A, G, GA, GB,	6LY8	9DX	6JT8, 6KR8, A, 6KV8,
		GC, GT, GX, Y,			6LB8, 6LQ8
		5881, 7581, 7581A	6LZ6	9QL	6ME6, 6MJ6
6L6GB	7AC	6L6, A, G, GA, GAY,	6M3	8GV	
		GC, GT, GX, Y,	6M5	9N	6CK6§
		5881, 7581, 7581A	6M6G	7S	6AG6G*
6L6GC	7AC	7581, 7581A	6M7G	7R	6K7§, G§, GT§,
6L6GT	7AC	6L6, A, G, GA, GAY,			GTX§, MG§
		GB, GC, GX, Y,	6M8G	8AU	6M8GT
		5881, 7581, 7581A	6M8GT	8AU	6M8G
6L6GX	7AC	6L6, A, G, GA, GAY,	6M11	12CA	
		GB, GC, GT, Y,	6MA6	8NP	
		5881, 7581, 7581A	6MB6	12FY	6JE6B, C, 6LZ6
6L6Y	7AC	6L6, A, G, GA, GAY,	6MB8	9FA	6LJ8§
		GB, GC, GT, GX,	6MC6	9QL	6MJ6
		5881, 7581, 7581A	6MD8	9RR	
6L7	7T	6L7G	6ME6	9QL	6JE6B, C, 6MJ6, 6LZ6
6L7G	7T	6L7	6ME8	9RU	
6LB6	12JF		6MF8	12DZ	
6LB8	9DX	6JT8, 6KR8, A, 6KV8,	6MG8	9DC	6EA8, 6U8, A, 6CQ8§
		6LQ8, 6LY8	6MJ6	9QL	
6LC6	8ML	6LH6, A	6MJ8	12HG	
6LC8	9QY		6MK8	9FG	6HS8, 6MK8A
6LE8	9QZ		6MK8A	9FG	6HS8, 6MK8
6LF6	12GW	6LV6	6ML8	9RQ	
6LF8	9DX	6AW8, A, 6JV8,	6MN8	12HU	
		6KS8, 6CX8*,	6MQ8	9AE	6EA8*, 6U8*, A*
		6GN8*, 6HF8*,	6MU8	9AE	
		6HZ8*, 6JA8*,	6MV8	9DX	
		6JE8*	6MY8	12DZ	6LU8
6LG6	12HL		6N3	9BM	6U3
6LH6	8ML	6LH6A	6N4	7CA	
6LH6A	8ML				

Tube Type	Basing	Replacement	Tube Type	Basing	Replacement
6N5	6R	6N5G, 6AB5, 6AB5/6N5	6SA7	8R	6SA7G, GT, GT/G, GTX, GTY, Y, 6SB7, Y, GTY
6N5G	6R	6N5, 6AB5, 6AB5/6N5	6SA7G	8R	6SA7, GT, GT/G, GTX, GTY, Y, 6SB7, Y, GTY
6N6	7AU	6N6G, 6N6, 6AB6G*			
6N6G	7AU	6N6, MG, 6AB6G*			
6N6MG	7AU	6N6, G, 6AB6G*	6SA7GT	8R	6SA7, G, GT/G, GTX, GTY, Y, 6SB7, Y, GTY
6N7	8B	6N7G, GT, GT/G, MG			
6N7G	8B	6N7, GT, GT/G, 6N7MG	6SA7GT/G	8R	6SA7, G, GT, GTX, GTY, Y, 6SB7, Y, GTY
6N7GT	8B	6N7, G, GT/G, MG			
6N7GT/G	8B	6N7, G, GT, MG	6SA7GTX	8R	6SA7, G, GT, GT/G, GTY, Y, 6SB7, Y, GTY
6N7MG	8B	6N7, G, GT, GT/G			
6N8	9T	6AD8, 6DC8	6SA7GTY	8R	6SA7, G, GT, GT/G, GTX, Y, 6SB7, Y, GTY
6P5G	6Q	6P5GT, GT/G			
6P5GT	6Q	6P5G, GT/G			
6P5GT/G	6Q	6P5G, GT	6SA7Y	8R	6SA7, G, GT, GT/G, GTX, GTY, 6SB7, Y, GTY
6P6	6AC				
6P7G	7U				
6Q4	9S		6SB7	8R	6SB7GTY, Y
6Q6	6Y	6Q6G	6SB7GTY	8R	6SB7, Y
6Q6G	6Y	6Q6	6SB7Y	8R	6SB7, GTY
6Q7	7V	6Q7G, GT, MG, 6B6, G, 6T7G*	6SC7	8S	6SC7GT, GTY
			6SC7GT	8S	6SC7, GTY
6Q7G	7V	6Q7, GT, MG, 6B6, G, 6T7G*	6SC7GTY	8S	6SC7, GT
			6SD7GT	8N	6SE7GT
6Q7GT	7V	6Q7, G, MG, 6B6, G, 6T7G*	6SE7GT	8N	6SD7GT
			6SF5	6AB	6SF5GT
6Q7MG	7V	6Q7, G, GT, 6B6, G, 6T7G*	6SF5GT	6AB	6SF5
			6SF7	7AZ	6SF7GT
6Q11	12BY		6SF7GT	7AZ	6SF7
6R3	9CB	6AF3*, 6AL3*, 6BR3*	6SG7	8BK	6SG7Y, 6SH7, GT, 6AB7*§, Y*§, 6AC7*§, A*§, Y*§, 6AJ7*§
6R4	9R				
6R6G	6AW				
6R7	7V	6R7G, GT, GT/G, MG			
6R7G	7V	6R7, GT, GT/G, MG	6SG7GT	8BK	6SG7, Y, 6SH7, GT, 6AB7*§, Y*§, 6AC7*§, A*§, Y*§, 6AJ7*§
6R7GT	7V	6R7, G, GT/G, MG			
6R7GT/G	7V	6R7, G, GT, MG			
6R7MG	7V	6R7, G, GT, GT/G	6SG7Y	8BK	6SG7, GT, 6SH7, GT, 6AB7*§, Y*§, 6AC7*§, A*§, Y*§, 6AJ7*§
6R8	9E	6T8, A			
6S2	9DT	6S2A			
6S2A	9DT	6S2	6SH7	8BK	6SH7GT, L, 6SG7, GT, Y, 6AB7*§, Y*§, 6AC7*§, A*§, Y*§, 6AJ7*§
6S4	9AC	6S4A			
6S4A	9AC				
6S6GT	5AK				
6S7	7R	6S7G, 6K7*, G*, GT*, GTX*, MG*			
6S7G	7R	6S7, 6K7*, G*, GT*, GTX*, MG*			
6S8GT	8CB				

§ May not work in all circuits.   * Parallel-filament circuits.
† Series circuit not requiring controlled warm-up time.

Tube Type	Basing	Replacement
6SH7GT	8BK	6SH7, L, 6SG7, GT, Y, 6AB7*§, Y*§, 6AC7*§, A*§, Y*§, 6AJ7*§
6SH7L	8BK	6SH7, GT, 6SG7, GT, Y, 6AB7*§, Y*§, 6AC7*§, A*§, Y*§, 6AJ7*§
6SJ7	8N	6SJ7GT, GTX, GTY, Y
6SJ7GT	8N	6SJ7, GTX, GTY, Y
6SJ7GTX	8N	6SJ7, GT, GTY, Y
6SJ7GTY	8N	6SJ7, GT, GTX, Y
6SJ7Y	8N	6SJ7, GT, GTX, GTY
6SK7	8N	6SG7, 6SK7GT, GT/G, GTX, GTY, Y, 6SS7*, GT*
6SK7G	8N	6SG7, 6SH7, 6SK7, GT, GT/G, GTX, GTY, Y, 6SS7*, GT*
6SK7GT	8N	6SG7, 6SH7, 6SK7, G, GT/G, GTX, GTY, Y, 6SS7*, GT*
6SK7GT/G	8N	6SK7, G, GT, GTX, GTY, Y, 6SS7*, GT*
6SK7GTX	8N	6SK7, G, GT, GT/G, GTY, Y, 6SS7*, GT*
6SK7GTY	8N	6SK7, G, GT, GT/G, GTX, Y, 6SS7*, GT*
6SK7Y	8N	6SK7, G, GT, GT/G, GTX, GTY, 6SS7*, GT*
6SL7A	8BD	6SL7GT, 6SL7, L
6SL7GT	8BD	6SL7A, GTY, L
6SL7GTY	8BD	6SL7A, GTY, L
6SL7L	8BD	6SL7A, GT, GTY
6SN7A	8BD	6SN7GT, GTA, GTB, GTY, L
6SN7GT	8BD	6SN7A, GTA, GTB, GTY, L
6SN7GTA	8BD	6SN7GTB
6SN7GTB	8BD	6SN7GTA*†
6SN7GTY	8BD	6SN7A, GT, GTA, GTB, L
6SN7L	8BD	6SN7A, GT, GTA, GTB, GTY
6SQ7	8Q	6SQ7G, GT, GT/G, 6SZ7*
6SQ7G	8Q	6SQ7, GT, GT/G, 6SZ7*
6SQ7GT	8Q	6SQ7, G, GT/G, 6SZ7*
6SQ7GT/G	8Q	6SQ7, G, GT, 6SZ7*
6SR7	8Q	6SR7G, GT, 6ST7*
6SR7G	8Q	6SR7, GT, 6ST7*

Tube Type	Basing	Replacement
6SR7GT	8Q	6SR7, G, 6ST7*
6SS7	8N	6SS7GT, 6SK7*, G*, GT*, GT/G*, GTX*, GTY*, Y*
6SS7GT	8N	6SS7, 6SK7*, G*, GT*, GT/G*, GTX*, GTY*, Y*
6ST7	8Q	6SR7, G*, GT*
6SU7GT	8BD	6SU7GTX, GTY
6SU7GTX	8BD	6SU7GT, GTY
6SU7GTY	8BD	6SU7GT, GTX
6SV7	7AZ	6SV7GT
6SV7GT	7AZ	6SV7
6SZ7	8Q	6SQ7*, G, GT*, GT/G*
6T4	7DK	6AF4§, A§, 6AN4§, 6DZ4§
6T5	6R	6G5, 6G5/6H5, 6H5, 6U5, 6U5/6G5
6T6	6Z	6T6GM
6T6GM	6Z	6T6
6T7G	7V	6B6*, 6B6G*, 6Q7*, G*, GT*, MG*
6T8	9E	6T8A, 6AK8
6T8A	9E	6T8*†, 6AK8*†
6T9	12FM	
6T10	12EZ	6AD10§
6U3	9BM	
6U4GT	4CG	6AS4GT, 6AX4GT, GTA, GTB, 6DA4, A, 6DM4, A, 6DQ4, 6DT4, 6W4GT, GTA, 6AU4GT*, GTA*, 6CQ4*, 6DE4*
6U5	6R	6G5, 6G5/6H5, 6H5, 6T5, 6U5/6G5
6U5/6G5	6R	6U5, 6G5, 6G5/6H5, 6H5, 6T5
6U6GT	7AC	6Y6G*, GA*, GT*
6U7G	7R	6K7, G, GT, GTX, MG, 6S7*, G*
6U8	9AE	6EA8, 6LN8, 6CQ8§, 6KD8*, 6MQ8*, 6U8A
6U8A	9AE	6EA8, 6LN8, 6CQ8§, 6KD8§, 6MQ8§, 6U8*†
6U10	12FE	6AC10§
6V3	9BD	6V3A
6V3A	9BD	6V3
6V4	9M	6CA4*
6V5G	6AO	6V5GT
6V5GT	6AO	6V5G

Tube Type	Basing	Replacement	Tube Type	Basing	Replacement
6V6	7AC	6V6G, GT, GTA, GT/G, GTX, GTY, GX, Y, 7408	6W7G	7R	6J7*, G*, GT*, GTX*, MG*
6V6G	7AC	6V6, GT, GTA, GT/G, GTX, GTY, GX, Y, 7408	6X4	5BS	6BX4, 6AV4*
			6X5	6S	6X5G, GT, GT/G, L, MG, 6AX5GT*, 6W5G*, GT*
6V6GT	7AC	6V6, G, GTA, GT/G, GTX, GTY, GX, Y, 7408	6X5G	6S	6X5, GT, GT/G, L, MG, GT*, 6W5G*, GT*
6V6GTA	7AC	6V6*†, G*†, GT*†, GT/G*†, GTX*†, GTY*†, GX*†, Y*†, 7408*†	6X5GT	6S	6X5, G, GT/G, L, MG, 6AX5GT*, 6W5G*, GT*
6V6GT/G	7AC	6V6, G, GT, GTA, GTX, GTY, GX, Y, 7408	6X5GT/G	6S	6X5, G, GT, L, MG, 5GT*, 6W5G*, GT*
6V6GTX	7AC	6V6, G, GT, GTA, GT/G, GTY, GX, Y, 7408	6X5L	6S	6X5, G, GT, GT/G, MG, 6AX5GT*, 6W5G*, GT*
6V6GTY	7AC	6V6, G, GT, GTA, GT/G, GTX, GX, GY, 7408	6X5MG	6S	6X5, G, GT, L, GT/G, 6AX5GT*, 6W5G*, GT*
6V6GX	7AC	6V6, G, GT, GTA, GT/G, GTY, GTX, Y, 7408	6X8	9AK	6X8A, 6AU8*§, A*§, 6AW8*§, A*§, 6EH8§
6V6Y	7AC	6V6, G, GT, GTA, GT/G, GTX, GTY, GX, 7408	6X8A	9AK	6X8*†, 6AU8*§, A*§, 6AW8*§, A*§, 6EH8§
6V7G	7V		6Y3	4AC	6Y3G
6V8	9AH		6Y3G	4AC	6Y3
6W4GT	4CG	6W4GTA, 6AS4GT, 6AX4GT, GTA, GTB, 6DA4, A, 6DM4, A, 6DQ4, 6DT4, 6U4GT, 6AU4GT*, GTA*, 6CQ4*, 6DE4*	6Y5	6J	6Y5G, GT, V
			6Y5G	6J	6Y5, GT, V
			6Y5GT	6J	6Y5, G, V
			6Y5V	6J	6Y5, G, GT
			6Y6G	7AC	6Y6GA, GT, 6U6GT*
			6Y6GA	7AC	6Y6G, GT, 6U6GT*
			6Y6GT	7AC	6Y6G, GA, 6U6GT*
			6Y7G	8B	
6W4GTA	4CG	6AX4GTA, GTB, 6DA4, A, 6DM4, A, 6DQ4, 6DT4, 6U4GT, 6AU4GT*, GTA*, 6CQ4*, 6DE4*	6Y9	10L	
			6Y10	12EZ	6AD10
			6Z3	4G	1V
			6Z4	5D	84/6Z4, 98
			6Z5	6K	12Z5, 6Z5/12Z5
			6Z5/12Z5	6K	6Z5, 12Z5
6W5	6S	6W5G, GT, 6AX5GT*	6Z6G	7Q	6Z6GT, MG
6W5G	6S	6W5, GT, 6AX5GT*	6Z6GT	7Q	6Z6G, MG
6W5GT	6S	6W5, G, 6AX5GT*	6Z6MG	7Q	6Z6G, GT
6W6	7AC	6W6GT, 6DG6GT, 6EF6*, 6EY6*, 6EZ5*	6Z7G	8B	
			6Z10	12BT	6J10
			6ZY5G	6S	6X5*, G*, GT*, GT/G*, L*, MG*
6W6GT	7AC	6W6, 6DG6GT, 6EF6*, 6EY6*, 6EZ5*	7A4	5AC	XXL
			7A5	6AA	
			7A6	7AJ	

§ May not work in all circuits.   * Parallel-filament circuits.
† Series circuit not requiring controlled warm-up time.

Tube Type	Basing	Replacement	Tube Type	Basing	Replacement
7A7	8V	7A7LM, 7H7, 7B7*	7S7	8BL	7J7
7A7LM	8V	7A7, 7H7, 7B7*	7T7	8V	7AG7*, 7V7*
7A8	8U	7B8*, 7B8LM*	7V7	8V	7G7, 7L7*, 7T7*
7AB7	8BO		7W7	8BJ	
7AD7	8V		7X6	7DX	
7AF7	8AC		7X7	8BZ	XXFM
7AG7	8V	7AH7, 7G7*, 7T7*	7Y4	5AB	7Z4*
7AH7	8V	7AG7, 7B7, 7H7*	7Z4	5AB	
7AJ7	8V	7C7*	8A8	9DC	9A8, 9EA8, 9U8, A
7AK7	8V		8AC9	12GN	
7AN7	9DD	7EK7	8AC10	12FE	8AC10A
7AU7	9A	6AU7, 6AX7§	8AC10A	12FE	
7B4	5AC	7A4§, XXL§	8AL9	12HE	
7B5	6AE	7B5LT, 7C5*, 7C5LT*	8AR11	12DM	8BQ11§
7B5LT	6AE	7B5, 7C5*, 7C5LT*	8AU8	9DX	8AU8A, 8AW8A, 8BA8A, 8BH8
7B6	8W	7B6LM, 7C6*	8AU8A	9DX	8AU8, 8AW8A, 8BA8A, 8BH8
7B6LM	8W	7B6, 7C6*	8AW8A	9DX	8AU8, A, 8BA8A, 8BH8, 8KS8, 8JV8
7B7	8V	7AH7, 7A7*, 7A7LM*, 7H7*	8B8	9EX	
7B8	8X	7B8LM, 7A8*	8B10	12B4	
7B8LM	8X	7B8, 7A8*	8BA8A	9DX	8AU8, A, 8AW8A, 8BH8
7C4	4AH		8BA11	12ER	
7C5	6AA	7C5LT, 7B5*, 7B5LT*	8BH8	9DX	8AU8, A, 8AW8A, 8BA8A
7C5LT	6AA	7C5, 7B5*, 7B5LT*	8BM11	12FU	
7C6	8W	7B6*, 7B6LM*	8BN8	9ER	
7C7	8V	7AJ7*, 7G7*, 7L7*	8BN11	12GF	
7D7	8AR		8BQ5	9CV	
7DJ8	9DE	7ES8	8BQ7A	9AJ	
7E5	8BN		8BQ11	12DM	8AR11§
7E6	8W		8BU11	12FP	
7E7	8AE	7R7	8CB11	12DM	
7ED7	9AQ		8CG7	9AJ	8FQ7§
7EK7	9DD	7AN7	8CM7	9ES	
7ES8	9DE	7DJ8	8CN7	9EN	
7EY6	7AC		8CS7	9EF	
7F7	8AC		8CW5	9CV	8CW5A
7F8	8BW		8CW5A	9CV	8CW5†
7FC7	9DD	7EK7	8CX8	9DX	8EB8, 8GN8, 8JE8
7G7	8V	7V7, 7AG7*, 7C7*, 7L7*	8CY7	9EF	
7G8	8BV		8EB8	9DX	8CX8, 8GN8, 8JE8
7GS7	9GF		8EM5	9HN	
7GV7	9KN		8ET7	9LT	
7H7	8V	7A7, LM, 7AH7*, 7B7*	8FQ7	9LP	
7HG8	9MP	8HG8	8GJ7	9QA	8GX7
7J7	8BL	7S7	8GK6	9GK	
7K7	8BF		8GN8	9DX	8CX8, 8EB8, 8JE8
7KY6	9GK		8GU7	9LP	
7KZ6	9GK		8GX7	9QA	8GJ7
7L7	8V	7C7*, 7G7*, 7V7*	8HA6	9NW	
7N7	8AC	7AF7*	8HG8	9MP	7HG8
7Q7	8AL				
7R7	8AE	7E7			

Tube Type	Basing	Replacement	Tube Type	Basing	Replacement
8JE8	9DX	8CX8, 8EB8, 8GN8	10AL11	12BU	
8JK8	9AJ		10BQ5	9CV	
8JL8	9DX		10C8	9DA	
8JT8	9DX		10CW5	9CV	
8JU8A	9PQ		10DA7	9EF	
8JV8	9DX	8AW8A, 8KS8	10DE7	9HF	10EW7
8KA8	9PV		10DR7	9HF	10FD7, 10FR7
8KR8	9DX		10DX8	9HX	
8KS8	9DX	8AU8, A, 8AW8A, 8JV8	10EB8	9DX	10GN8, 10HF8, 10JA8, 11JE8
8LC8	9QY		10EG7	8BD	10EM7
8LE8	9QZ		10EM7	8BD	10EG7
8LS6	9GK		10EW7	9HF	
8LT8	9RL		10FD7	9HF	10FR7
8MU8	9AE		10FR7	9HF	10FD7
8SN7GTB	8BD		10GF7	9QD	10GF7A
9A8	9DC	8A8, 9EA8, 9U8, 9U8A	10GF7A	9QD	10GF7
			10GK6	9GK	
9AH9	12HJ		10GN8	9DX	10EB8, 10HF8, 11JE8, 10LZ8, 10JY8, 10JA8
9AK8	9E				
9AK10	12FE				
9AM10	12FE		10HA6	9NW	
9AQ8	9DE		10HF8	9DX	10EB8, 10GN8, 11JE8, 10LZ8, 10JY8, 10JA8
9AU7	9A				
9BJ11	12FU				
9BM5	7DQ		10J10	12BT	
9BR7	9CF		10JA5	12EY	
9BR8	9FA	9CL8§	10JA8	9DX	11JE8, 10EB8, 10GN8, 10HF8, 10JY8
9BW6	9AM				
9CG8A	9GF	9BR8†§	10JT8	9DX	10KR8, 10LB8*, 10LW8, 10LY8, 11KV8, 11LQ8
9CL8	9FX	9BR8§†			
9DZ8	9JE				
9EA8	9AE	8A8, 9U8A, 9A8†, 9U8†	10JY8	9DX	10EB8, 10GN8, 10HF8, 10LZ8, 11JE8, 10JA8
9EF6	7S				
9EN7	9LM		10KR8	9DX	10LW8, 10JT8, 10LB8, 11KV8, 11LQ8
9GB8	9DA				
9GH8A	9AE	9EA8	10KU8	9LT	
9GV8	9LY		10LB8	9DX	10LW8, 10KR8, 10JT8, 11KV8, 11LQ8
9JW8	9DC				
9KC6	9RF				
9KX6	9GK		10LE8	9QZ	
9KZ8	9FZ		10LW8	9DX	10JT8, 10KR8, 10LB8, 11KV8, 11LQ8
9LA6	9GK				
9ML8	9RQ		10LY8	9DX	10JT8
9MN8	12HU		10LZ8	9DX	10EB8, 10GN8, 10HF8, 11JE8, 10JY8
9U8	9AE	8A8, 9U8A, 9A8, 9EA8			
9U8A	9AE	8A8, 9U8†, 9A8†, 9EA8	10T10	12EZ	
			10X	4D	10, 10Y
9X8	9AK		10Y	4D	10, 10X
10	4D	10X, 10Y	10Z10	12BT	

§ May not work in all circuits.   * Parallel-filament circuits.
† Series circuit not requiring controlled warm-up time.

Tube Type	Basing	Replacement
11	4F	
11AR11	12DM	11BQ11§
11BM8	9EX	
11BQ11	12DM	11AR11§
11BT11	12GS	
11C5	7CV	12DM5
11CA11	12HN	
11CF11	12HW	
11CH11	12GS	
11CY7	9EF	
11DS5	7BZ	
11FY7	12EO	
11HM7	9BF	
11JE8	9DX	10EB8, 10GN8, 10HF8, 10JA8, 10LZ8, 10JY8
11KV8	9DX	10JT8, 10KR8, 10LW8, 10LB8, 11LQ8
11LQ8	9DX	11KV8, 10LB8, 10LW8, 10KR8, 10JT8
11LT8	9RL	
11LY6	9GK	12BY7A†
11MS8	9LY	
11Y9	10L	
12	4D	
12A	4D	12A/112A, 112A
12A/112A	4D	12A, 112A
12A4	9AG	
12A5	7F	
12A6	7AC	12A6G, GT, GTY, Y, 12V6GT*§
12A6G	7AC	12A6, GT, GTY, Y, 12V6GT*§
12A6GT	7AC	12A6, G, GTY, Y, 12V6GT*§
12A6GTY	7AC	12A6, G, GT, Y, 12V6GT*§
12A6Y	7AC	12A6, G, GT, GTY, 12V6GT*§
12A7	7K	
12A8	8A	12A8G, GT
12A8G	8A	12A8, GT
12A8GT	8A	12A8, G
12AB5	9EU	
12AC5	8GW	
12AC6	7BK	12AF6§
12AC10A	12FE	
12AD5	9AZ	
12AD6	7CH	12AG6
12AD7	9A	12AX7*, A*, 12BZ7*, 12DF7*, 12DM7*, 12DT7*, 7025*, A*
12AE6	7BT	12AE6A, 12FT6
12EA6A	7BT	12AE6, 12FT6
12AE7	9A	
12AE10	12EZ	13V10
12AF3	9CB	12BR3
12AF6	7BK	12BL6, 12AC6, 12EK6§
12AG6	7CH	12AD6
12AH6	7BK	
12AH7GT	8BE	
12AH8	9BP	
12AJ6	7BT	
12AJ7	9CA	
12AL5	6BT	
12AL8	9GS	
12AL11	12BU	
12AQ5	7BZ	12BM5*
12AS5	7CV	12CA5*, 12R5*
12AT6	7BT	12AT6A, 12AV6, A, 12BK6, 12BT6
12AT6A	7BT	12AV6A, 12AT6*†, 12BK6*†, 12BT6*†
12AT7	9A	12AZ7*, A*
12AU6	7BK	12AU6A, 12BA6, A, 12AW6§
12AU6A	7BK	12BA6A, 12AU6*†
12AU7	9A	12AU7A, 12AX7§, A§
12AU7A	9A	12AU7, 12AX7§, A§
12AU8	9DX	
12AV5GA	6CK	12AV5GT*†
12AV5GT	6CK	12AV5GA
12AV6	7BT	12AV6A, 12AT6, A, 12BK6, 12BT6
12AV6A	7BT	12AT6A, 12AV6*†, 12BK6*†, 12BT6*†
12AV7	9A	
12AW6	7CM	12AU6§, 12AU6A§
12AX3	12BL	
12AX4GT	4CG	12AX4GTA, GTB, 12D4, 12D4A, 12DM4, A, 12DQ4
12AX4GTA	4CG	12AX4GTB, 12D4, A, 12DM4, A, 12DQ4, 12AX4GT*†
12AX4GTB	4CG	12D4A, 12DM4, A, 12DQ4
12AX7	9A	12AX7A, 12DF7, 12DT7, 7025, A, 12AD7*, 12AU7§, A§, 12BZ7*, 12DM7*
12AX7A	9A	12AX7, 12DF7, 12DT7, 7025, A, 12AD7*, 12AU7§, A§, 12BZ7*, 12DM7*

Tube Type	Basing	Replacement
12AY3	9HP	12AY3A, 12BS3, A, 12CK3, 12CL3, 12DW4A
12AY3A	9HP	12AY3, 12BS3, A, 12CK3, 12CL3, 12DW4A
12AY7	9A	
12AZ7	9A	12AZ7A, 12AT7*
12AZ7A	9A	12AZ7*†, 12AT7*
12B3	9BD	
12B4	9AG	12B4A
12B4A	9AG	12B4*†
12B6M	6Y	
12B7	8V	12B7ML, 14A7, 14H7, 14A7/12B7, 14A7ML, 14A7ML/12B7ML
12B7ML	8V	12B7, 14A7, 14H7, 14A7/12B7, 14A7ML, 14A7ML/12B7ML
12B8	8T	12B8GT
12B8GT	8T	12B8
12BA6	7BK	12AU6, A, 12BA6A, 12BZ6§
12BA6A	7BK	12AU6A, 12BA6*†
12BA7	8CT	
12BD6	7BK	12BA6, 12BA6A
12BE3	12GA	12BE3A
12BE3A	12GA	12BE3
12BE6	7CH	12BE6A, 12CS6
12BE6A	7CH	12BE6*†, 12CS6*†
12BF6	7BT	12BU6
12BF11	12EZ	
12BH7	9A	12BH7A
12BH7A	9A	12BH7*†
12BK5	9BQ	
12BK6	7BT	12AT6, A, 12AV6, A, 12BT6
12BL6	7BK	12AF6, 12EK6§
12BM5	7DQ	12AQ5*
12BN6	7DF	12BN6A
12BN6A	7DF	12BN6*†
12BQ6GA	6AM	12BQ6GTA, GTB, 12BQ6GTB/12CU6, 12CU6, 12DQ6, A, B, 12GW6
12BQ6GT	6AM	12BQ6GA, GTA, GTB, 12BQ6GTB/12CU6, 12CU6, 12DQ6, A, B, 12GW6

Tube Type	Basing	Replacement
12BQ6GTA	6AM	12BQ6GA, GTB, 12BQ6GTB/12CU6, 12CU6, 12DQ6, A, B, 12GW6
12BQ6GTB	6AM	12BQ6GTB/12CU6, 12CU6, 12DQ6A, B, 12GW6
12BQ6GTB/ 12CU6	6AM	12BQ6GTB, 12CU6, 12DQ6, A, B, 12GW6
12BR3	9CB	
12BR7	9CF	12BR7A
12BR7A	9CF	12BR7*†
12BS3	9HP	12BS3A, 12CK3, 12CL3, 12DW4
12BS3A	9HP	12BS3, 12CK3, 12CL3, 12DW4
12BT3	12BL	
12BT6	7BT	12AT6, A, 12AV6, A, 12BK6
12BU6	7BT	12BF6
12BV7	9BF	12BY7, A, 12DQ7
12BV11	12HB	
12BW4	9DJ	
12BX6	9AQ	13EC7*
12BY3	9CB	
12BY7	9BF	12BY7A, 12BV7, 12DQ7
12BY7A	9BF	12DQ7, 12BY7*†, 12BV7*†
12BZ6	7CM	12BA6§, 12BA6A§
12BZ7	9A	
12C5	7CV	12C5/12CU5, 12CU5, 12R5, 12AS5*, 12DM5*
12C5/12CU5	7CV	12C5, 12CU5, 12R5, 12AS5*, 12DM5*
12C8	8E	12C8Y
12C8Y	8E	12C8
12CA5	7CV	12EH5, 12AS5*, 12ED5*, 12FX5*
12CK3	9HP	12CL3, 12DW4A
12CL3	9HP	12CK3, 12DW4A
12CM6	9CK	
12CN5	7CV	
12CR5	9HC	
12CR6	7EA	
12CS5	9CK	12DW5, 12CM6*
12CS6	7CH	12BE6, 12BE6A
12CT3	9RX	
12CT8	9DA	

§ May not work in all circuits.   * Parallel-filament circuits.
† Series circuit not requiring controlled warm-up time.

Tube Type	Basing	Replacement	Tube Type	Basing	Replacement
12CU5	7CV	12C5, 12C5/12CU5, 12R5, 12AS5*, 12DM5*	12DZ8	9JE	12FY8*
			12E5GT	6Q	12J5, 12J5GT
			12EA6	7BK	12DZ6, 12EK6
12CU6	6AM	12BQ6GTB/12CU6, 12BQ6GTB, 12DQ6, A, B, 12GW6	12EC8	9FA	
			12ED5	7CV	12FX5, 12CA5*, 12EH5*
12CX6	7BK	12EZ6			
12CY6	7BK		12EF6	7S	
12D4	4CG	12D4A, 12AX4GTB, 12DM4, A, 12DQ4	12EG6	7CH	
			12EH5	7CV	12CA5, 12ED5*, 12FX5*
12D4A	4CG	12DM4, A, 12DQ4	12EK6	7BK	12DZ6, 12EA6
12DB5	9GR		12EL6	7FB	
12DE8	9HG		12EM6	9HV	
12DF5	9BS		12EN6	7S	12L6GT, 12W6GT
12DF7	9A	12AX7, A, 12DT7, 7025, A, 12AD7*, 12BZ7*, 12DM7*	12EQ7	9LQ	12KL8§
			12EZ6	7BK	12CX6
			12F5	5M	12F5GT
12DJ8	9DE		12F5GT	5M	12F5
12DK5	9GT		12F8	9FH	
12DK6	7CM		12FA6	7CH	
12DK7	9HZ		12FB5	9CV	
12DL8	9HR	12DS7§, A§	12FK6	7BT	12FM6
12DM4	4CG	12DM4A, 12D4A, 12DQ4	12FM6	7BT	12FK6
			12FQ7	9LP	
12DM4A	4CG		12FQ8	9KT	
12DM5	7CV	11C5, 12AS5*, 12C5*, 12C5/12CU5*, 12CU5*, 12R5*	12FR8	9KU	
			12FT6	7BT	12AE6, 12AE6A
			12FV7	9A	
12DM7	9A	12AD7*, 12AX7*, 12AX7A*, 12BZ7*, 12DF7*, 12DT7*, 7025*, A*	12FX5	7CV	12ED5, 12EH5*
			12FX8	9KV	12FX8A
			12FX8A	9KV	12FX8
			12FY8	9EX	
12DQ4	4CG		12G4	6BG	12H4
12DQ6	6AM	12DQ6A, B, 12GW6	12G8	9CZ	
12DQ6A	6AM	12DQ6B, 12GW6	12G11	12BU	
12DQ6B	6AM	12GW6	12GA6	7CH	
12DQ7	9BF	12BY7A, 12BV7*†	12GC6	8JX	
12DS7	9JU	12DS7A	12GE5	12BJ	
12DS7A	9JU	12DS7	12GJ5	9QK	
12DT5	9HN		12GN6	7FW	
12DT6	7EN		12GN7	9BF	12GN7A, 12HG7*†
12DT7	9A	12AX7, A, 12DF7, 7025, A, 12AD7*, 12BZ7*, 12DM7*	12GN7A	9BF	12HG7*†
			12GT5	9NZ	12GT5A
			12GT5A	9NZ	12GT5
12DT8	9AJ		12GV5	12DR	
12DU7	9JX		12GW6	6AM	12DQ6B
12DV7	9JY		12H4	7DW	
12DV8	9HR		12H6	7Q	
12DW4A	9HP	12CK3, 12CL3	12HE7	12FS	
12DW5	9CK		12HG7	9BF	12GN7*, A†
12DW7	9A	7247	12HL5	9QW	
12DW8	9JC		12HL7	9BF	
12DY8	9JD		12HU8	9NJ	
12DZ6	7BK	12EA6, 12EK6	12J5	6Q	12J5GT

Tube Type	Basing	Replacement	Tube Type	Basing	Replacement
12J5GT	6Q	12J5	12SF5	6AB	12SF5GT
12J7	7R	12J7G, GT, GT/G	12SF5GT	6AB	12SF5
12J7G	7R	12J7, GT, GT/G	12SF7	7AZ	12SF7GT, Y
12J7GT	7R	12J7, G, GT/G	12SF7GT	7AZ	12SF7, Y
12J7GT/G	7R	12J7, G, GT	12SF7Y	7AZ	12SF7, GT
12J8	9GC		12SG7	8BK	12SG7GT, Y
12JB6	9QL	12JB6A	12SG7GT	8BK	12SG7, Y
12JB6A	9QL	12JB6	12SG7Y	8BK	12SG7, GT
12JF5	12JH		12SH7	8BK	12SH7GT
12JN6	12FK	12JN6A	12SH7GT	8BK	12SH7
12JN6A	12FK	12JN6	12SJ7	8N	12SJ7GT
12JN8	9FA		12SJ7GT	8N	12SJ7
12JQ6	9RA		12SK7	8N	12SK7G, GT, GT/G, GTY, Y
12JS6	12FY				
12JT6	9QU	12JT6A	12SK7G	8N	12SK7, GT, GT/G, GTY, Y
12JT6A	9QU	12JT6			
12K5	7FD		12SK7GT	8N	12SK7, G, GT/G, GTY, Y
12K7G	7R	12K7GT, GT/G			
12K7GT	7R	12K7G, GT/G	12SK7GT/G	8N	12SK7, G, GT, GTY, Y
12K7GT/G	7R	12K7G, GT	12SK7GTY	8N	12SK7, G, GT, GT/G, Y
12K8	8K	12K8GT, Y			
12K8GT	8K	12K8, Y	12SK7Y	8N	12SK7, G, GT, GT/G, GTY
12K8Y	8K	12K8, GT			
12KL8	9LQ		12SL7GT	8BD	
12L6GT	7AC	12EN6, 12W6GT	12SN7GT	8BD	12SN7GTA, 12SX7GT
12L8GT	8BU		12SN7GTA	8BD	
12MD8	9RQ		12SQ7	8Q	12SQ7G, GT, GT/G
12Q7	7V	12Q7G, GT, GT/G, 12G7G	12SQ7G	8Q	12SQ7, GT, GT/G
			12SQ7GT	8Q	12SQ7, G, GT/G
12Q7G	7V	12Q7, GT, GT/G, 12G7G	12SQ7GT/G	8Q	12SQ7, G, GT
			12SR7	8Q	12SR7GT, 12SW7, GT
12Q7GT	7V	12Q7, G, GT/G, 12G7G	12SR7GT	8Q	12SR7, 12SW7, GT
			12SW7	8Q	12SW7GT, 12SR7, GT
12Q7GT/G	7V	12Q7, G, GT, 12G7G	12SW7GT	8Q	12SW7, 12SR7, GT
12R5	7CV		12SX7GT	8BD	12SN7GT, GTA
12S7	8GX		12SY7	8R	12SY7GT, 12SA7, G, GT, GT/G, GTY, Y
12S8	8CB	12S8G, GT			
12S8G	8CB	12S8, GT			
12S8GT	8CB	12S8, G	12SY7GT	8R	12SY7, 12SA7, G, GT, GT/G, GTY, Y
12SA7	8R	12SA7G, GT, GT/G, GTY, Y, 12SY7, GT			
			12T10	12EZ	
12SA7G	8R	12SA7, GT, GT/G, GTY, Y, 12SY7, GT	12U7	9A	
			12V6GT	7AC	12A6*§, G*§, GT*§, GTY*§, Y*§
12SA7GT	8R	12SA7, G, GT/G, GTY, Y, 12SY7, GT			
			12W6GT	7AC	12EN6, 12L6GT
12SA7GT/G	8R	12SA7, G, GT, GTY, Y, 12SY7, GT	12X4	5BS	
			12Z3	4G	14Z3
12SA7GTY	8R	12SA7, G, GT, GT/G, Y, 12SY7, GT	12Z5	6K	6Z5, 6Z5/12Z5
			13	4C	5X3, 80, 83V, 88
12SA7Y	8R	12SA7, G, GT, GT/G, GTY, GT	13CM5	8GT	
			13CW4	12AQ	
			13DE7	9HF	15EW7
12SC7	8S		13DR7	9HF	13FD7, 13FR7

§ May not work in all circuits.   * Parallel-filament circuits.
† Series circuit not requiring controlled warm-up time.

Tube Type	Basing	Replacement	Tube Type	Basing	Replacement
13EC7	9AQ	12BX6*	14N7	8AC	14AF7*
13EM7	8BP	15EA7	14Q7	8AL	
13FD7	9HF	13FR7	14R7	8AE	14E7
13FM7	12EJ		14S7	8BL	14J7
13FR7	9HF	13FD7	14V7	8V	
13GB5	9NH		14W7	8BJ	
13GC8	9KZ		14X7	8BZ	
13GF7	9QD	13GF7A	14Y4	5AB	
13GF7A	9QD	13GF7	14Y7	9Q	
13J10	12BT	13Z10/13J10	14Z3	4G	12Z3
13JZ8	12DZ	13JZ8A	15	5F	
13JZ8A	12DZ		15A6	9AR	
13V10	12EZ	12AE10	15A8	8GS	
13Z10	12BT	13Z10/13J10	15AB9	10N	17AB9
14	5E		15AF11	12DP	15BD11, A
14A4	5AC		15BD11	12DP	15BD11A, 15AF11
14A5	6AA		15BD11A	12DP	15BD11, 15AF11
14A7	8V	12B7, ML, 14H7, 14A7/12B7, 14A7ML, 14A7ML/12B7ML	15CW5	9CV	
			15DQ8	9HX	
			15EA7	8BD	13EM7
14A7ML	8V	12B7, ML, 14A7, 14A7/12B7, 14A7ML/12B7ML, 14H7	15EW6	7CM	
			15EW7	9HF	
			15FM7	12EJ	
			15FY7	12EO	
14A7/12B7	8V	12B7, ML, 14A7, 14H7, 14A7ML, 14A7ML/12B7ML	15HB6	9NW	
			15KY8	9QT	15KY8A, 15MX8
			15KY8A	9QT	15KY8, 15MX8
14A7ML/ 12B7ML	8V	12B7, ML, 14A7, ML, 14A7/12B7, 14H7	15LE8	9QZ	
			15MF8	12DZ	
			15MX8	9QT	15KY8A
14AF7	8AC	XXD, 14N7*	16	4B	16B, 81
14B6	8W		16A5	9BL	15CW5
14B8	8X		16A8	9EX	
14BL11	12GC		16AK9	12GZ	
14BR11	12GL		16AQ3	9CB	
14C5	6AA		16B	4B	16, 81
14C7	8V		16BQ11	12DM	
14DA7	9EF		16BX11	12CA	
14E6	8W		16GK6	9GK	
14E7	8AE	14R7	16GK8	9JE	
14F7	8AC		16GY5	12DR	
14F8	8BW		16KA6	12GH	
14G6	9Z		16LU8	12DZ	16LU8A, 16MY8
14GT8	9KR	14GT8A, 14JG8	16LU8A	12DZ	16LU8, 16MY8
14GT8A	9KR	14GTB†, 14JG8†	16MY8	12DZ	16LU8A
14H7	8V	12B7, ML, 14A7, 14A7/12B7, 14A7ML, 14A7ML/12B7ML	16Y9	10L	
			17	5A	
			17A8	9DC	19EA8, 19EA8A
			17AB9	10N	15AB9
14J7	8BL	14S7	17AB10	12BT	
14JG8	9KR	14GT8, 14GT8A	17AV5GA	6CK	
14K7	8GY		17AX3	12BL	
14L7	8GZ		17AX4GT	4CG	17AX4GTA, 17D4, A, 17DM4, A, 17DQ4

Tube Type	Basing	Replacement	Tube Type	Basing	Replacement
17AX4GTA	4CG	17D4, A, 17DM4, A, 17DQ4	17H3	9FK	
			17HC8	9EX	
17AY3	9HP	17AY3A, 17BS3, A, 17CK3, 17CL3, 17DW4A	17JB6	9QL	17JB6A
			17JB6A	9QL	17JB6
			17JF6	9QL	
17AY3A	9HP	17AY3, 17BS3, A, 17CK3, 17CL3, 17DW4A	17JG6	9QU	17JG6A, 17KV6
			17JG6A	9QU	17JG6, 17KV6
			17JK8	9AJ	
17BE3	12GA	17BE3A, 17BZ3	17JM6	12FJ	17JM6A
17BE3A	12GA	17BE3, 17BZ3	17JM6A	12FJ	17JM6
17BF11	12EZ	17BF11A	17JN6	12FK	17JN6A
17BF11A	12EZ	17BF11	17JN6A	12FK	17JN6
17BH3	9HP	17BH3A	17JQ6	9RA	
17BH3A	9HP	17BH3	17JR6	9QU	17JG6, A
17BQ6GTB	6AM	17DQ6, A, B, 17GW6	17JT6	9QU	17JT6A
17BR3	9CB		17JT6A	9QU	17JT6
17BS3	9HP	17BS3A, 17CK3, 17CL3, 17DW4A	17JZ8	12DZ	17JZ8A
			17JZ8A	12DZ	
17BS3A	9HP	17BS3, 17CK3, 17CL3, 17DW4A	17KV6	9QU	17KV6A
			17KV6A	9QU	
17BW3	12FX	17AX3*, 17BE3*, A*	17L6GT	7AC	17W6GT
17BZ3	12FX	17BE3, A	17LD8	9QT	
17C5	7CV	17CU5, 17R5	17R5	7CV	
17C8	9T		17W6GT	7AC	17L6GT
17C9	10F	17C9A	17X10	12BT	
17C9A	10F	17C9†	17Z3	9CB	
17CA5	7CV		18	6B	
17CK3	9HP	17CL3, 17DW4A	18A5	6CK	
17CL3	9HP	17CK3, 17DW4A	18AJ10	12EZ	
17CQ4	4CG	17DE4	18DZ8	9JE	
17CT3	9RX		18FW6	7BK	18FW6A, 18GD6, 18GD6A
17CU5	7CV	17C5, 17R5			
17D4	4CG	17D4A, 17AX4GTA, 17DM4, A, 17DQ4	18FW6A	7BK	18GD6A, 18FW6†, 18GD6†
17D4A	4CG	17DM4, A, 17DQ4	18FX6	7CH	18FX6A
17DE4	4CG	17CQ4	18FX6A	7CH	18FX6†
17DM4	4CG	17DM4A, 17D4A, 17DQ4	18FY6	7BT	18FY6A, 18GE6, 18GE6A
17DM4A	4CG		18FY6A	7BT	18GE6A, 18FY6†, 18GE6†
17DQ4	4CG				
17DQ6	6AM	17DQ6A, B, 17GW6	18GB5	9NH	
17DQ6A	6AM	17DQ6B, 17GW6	18GD6	7BK	18GD6A, 18FW6, 18FW6A
17DQ6B	6AM	17GW6			
17DW4A	9HP	17CK3, 17CL3	18GD6A	7BK	18FW6A, 18GD6†, 18FW6†
17EW8	9AJ				
17GE5	12BJ		18GE6	7BT	18GE6A, 18FY6, 18FY6A
17GJ5	9QK	17GJ5A			
17GJ5A	9QK	17GJ5	18GE6A	7BT	18FY6A, 18GE6†, 18FY6†
17GT5	9NZ	17GT5A			
17GT5A	9NZ	17GT5			
17GV5	12DR		18GV8	9LY	
17GW6	6AM	17DQ6B	18HB8	9ME	
			19	6C	

§ May not work in all circuits.   * Parallel-filament circuits.
† Series circuit not requiring controlled warm-up time.

Tube Type	Basing	Replacement	Tube Type	Basing	Replacement
19AQ5	7BZ		21JS6A	12FY	
19AU4	4CG	19AU4GT, 19AU4GTA, 17CQ4, 17DE4	21JV6	12FK	
			21JZ6	12GD	
			21KA6	12GH	
19AU4GT	4CG	19AU4, 19AU4GTA, 17CQ4, 17DE4	21KQ6	9RJ	
			21LG6	12HL	21LG6A
19AU4GTA	4CG		21LG6A	12HL	21LG6
19BG6G	5BT	19BG6GA	21LR8	9QT	
19BG6GA	5BT	19BG6G	21LU8	12DZ	21MY8
19C8	9E	19T8, 19T8A	21MY8	12DZ	21LU8
19CG3	12HF		22	4K	
19CL8A	9FX	19CL8B, 19JN8	22BH3	9HP	22BH3A
19CL8B	9FX	19CL8A†, 19JN8†	22BH3A	9HP	22BH3
19CS4	8JT		22BW3	12FX	25CG3
19D8	9CA		22DE4	4CG	
19DE3	12HX		22JF6	9QL	22KM6
19DE7	9HF	19EW7, 20EW7	22JG6	9QU	22JG6A, 22JR6
19DK3	9SG		22JG6A	9QU	22JG6, 22JR6
19DQ3	12HF		22JR6	9QU	
19EA8	9AE	19EA8A, 17A8	22JU6	9QL	
19EA8A	9AE	19EA8†, 17A8†	22KM6	9QL	
19EW7	9HF	20EW7	22KV6A	9QL	
19EZ8	9KA		23JS6A	12FY	
19FX5	7CV		23MB6	12FY	
19GQ7	9RB		23Z9	12GZ	
19HR6	7BK		24A	5E	24S, 35§, 35/51§, 35S§, 51S§, 35S/51S§
19HS6	7BK				
19HV8	9FA				
19J6	7BF		24BF11	12EZ	
19JN8	9FA	19CL8A, 19CL8B	24GA7	12EB	
19KG8	9LY		24JE6A	9QL	24LQ6
19Q9	10H		24JZ8	12DZ	25JZ8
19T8	9E	19T8A, 19C8	24LQ6	9QL	24JE6A
19T8A	9E	19T8†, 19C8†	24LZ6	9QL	
19V8	9AH		24S	5E	24A, 35§, 35/51§, 51§, 35S§, 51S§, 35S/51S§
19X3	9BM				
19X8	9AK				
19Y3	9BM	19X3	25	6M	25S, 1B5, 1B5/25S
20	4D		25A6	7S	25A6G, GT, GT/G, MG
20AQ3	9CB				
20EQ7	9LG		25A6G	7S	25A6, GT, GT/G, MG
20EW7	9HF	19EW7	25A6GT	7S	25A6, G, GT/G, MG
20EZ7	9MJ		25A6GT/G	7S	25A6, G, GT, MG
20J8	8H		25A6MG	7S	25A6, G, GT, GT/G
20LF6	12GW		25A7G	8F	25A7GT, GT/G
21A6	9AS	21B6	25A7GT	8F	25A7G, GT/G
21A7	8AR		25A7GT/G	8F	25A7G, GT
21B6	9AS	21A6	25AC5G	6Q	25AC5GT, GT/G
21EX6	5BT	25CD6GB	25AC5GT	6Q	25AC5G, GT/G
21GY5	12DR		25AC5GT/G	6Q	25AC5G, GT
21HB5	12BJ	21HB5A	25AV5GA	6CK	25AV5GT
21HB5A	12BJ	21HB5	25AV5GT	6CK	25AV5GA
21HD5	12ES		25AX4GT	4CG	25D4
21HJ5	12FL		25B5	6D	

Tube Type	Basing	Replacement	Tube Type	Basing	Replacement
25B6	7S	25B6G, GT	25L6	7AC	25L6G, GT, 25L6GT/ G, 25W6GT
25B6G	7S	25B6, GT			
25B6GT	7S	25B6, G	25L6G	7AC	25L6, GT, GT/G, 25W6GT
25B8	8T	25B8GT			
25B8GT	8T	25B8	25L6GT	7AC	25L6, G, GT/G, 25W6GT
25BK5	9BQ				
25BQ6GA	6AM	25BQ6GTB, GTB/ 25CU6, 25CU6, 25DQ6, A	25L6GT/G	7AC	25L6, G, GT, 25W6GT
			25N6	7W	25N6G
			25N6G	7W	25N6
25BQ6GT	6AM	25BQ6GA, GTB, 25BQ6GTB/25CU6, 25CU6, 25DQ6, A	25S	6M	25, 1B5, 1B5/25S
			25U4GT	4CG	25AX4GT, 25D4, 25W4GT
25BQ6GTB	6AM	25BQ6GTB/25CU6, 25CU6, 25DQ6, A	25W4GT	4CG	25AX4GT, 25D4, 25U4GT
25BQ6GTB/ 25CU6	6AM	25BQ6GTB, 25CU6, A	25W6GT	7AC	25L6, G, GT, GT/G
			25X6GT	7Q	
25BR3	9CB		25Y4	5AA	25Y4GT
25C5	7CV		25Y4GT	5AA	25Y4
25C6G	7AC	25C6GA	25Y5	6E	25Z5, MG
25C6GA	7S	25C6G	25Z3	4G	
25CA5	7C	25C5, 25EH5	25Z4	5AA	25Z4GT
25CD6G	5BT	25CD6GA, GB, 25DN6, 21EX6	25Z4GT	5AA	25Z4
			25Z5	6E	25Z5MG, 25Y5
25CD6GA	5BT	25CD6GB, 25DN6, 21EX6	25Z5MG	6E	25Z5, 25Y5
			25Z6	7Q	25Z6G, GT, GT/G, MG
25CD6GB	5BT	21EX6			
25CG3	12HF		25Z6G	7Q	25Z6, GT, GT/G, MG
25CK3	9HP		25Z6GT	7Q	25Z6, G, GT/G, MG
25CM3	9HP		25Z6GT/G	7Q	25Z6, G, GT, MG
25CR5	9HC		25Z6MG	7Q	25Z6, G, GT, GT/G
25CT3	9RX		26	4D	
25CU6	6AM	25BQ6GTB/25CU6, 25BQ6GTB, 25DQ6, A	26A6	7BK	26CG6
			26A7	8BU	26A7GT
			26A7GT	8BU	26A7
25D4	4CG		26B6	7CH	26D6
25D8GT	8AF		26BK6	7BT	
25DK3	9SG		26C6	7BT	
25DK4	5BQ		26CG6	7BK	26A6
25DN6	5BT	25CD6GB, 21EX6	26D6	7CH	26B6
25DQ6	6AM	25DQ6A	26E6G	7S	
25DQ6A	6AM		26HU5	8NB	
25DT5	9HN		26LW6	8NC	
25E5	8GT		26LX6	12JA	
25EC6	5BT	25CD6GB, 21EX6	26Z5	9BS	
25EH5	7CV	25CA5	27	5A	27S, 56, 56S, 27A*
25F5	7CV	25F5A	27A	5A	27*, 27S*
25F5A	7CV	25F5†	27GB5	9NH	28GB5
25FY8	9EX		27KG6	9RJ	
25GF6	6AM		27S	5A	27, 56, 56S, 27A*
25HX5	9SB		28D7	8BS	
25JQ6	9RA		28GB5	9NH	27GB5
25JZ8	12DZ	24JZ8	28HA6	9NW	

§ May not work in all circuits.   * Parallel-filament circuits.
† Series circuit not requiring controlled warm-up time.

Tube Type	Basing	Replacement
28HD5	12ES	30HD5
28Z5	6BJ	
29GK6	9GK	
29KQ6	9RJ	29LE6
29LE6	9RJ	29KQ6
30	4D	
30A5	7CV	35C5, 35C5A
30AE3	9CB	
30AG11	12DA	
30CW5	9CV	
30HD5	12ES	28HD5
30HJ5	12FL	
30JZ6	12GD	
30KD6	12GW	
30MB6	12FY	
31	4D	
31A3	8HB	
31AL10	12HR	
31BX7GT	8BD	
31JS6A	12FY	31JS6C
31JS6C	12FY	31JS6A
31LQ6	9QL	
31LR8	9QT	
31LZ6	9Q6	
32	4K	1A4, P, T, 1B4, G, P, T, 34, 951, 1C4*, 1K4*
32A8	9EX	
32ET5	7CV	32ET5A, 34GD5, A
32ET5A	7CV	32ET5†, 34GD5A
32GA7	12EB	
32HQ7	12HT	
32L7GT	8Z	
33	5K	
33GT7	12FC	
33GY7	12FN	33GY7A
33GY7A	12FN	33GY7
33HE7	12FS	
33JR6	9QU	
33JV6	12FK	
34	4M	1A4, P, T, 1B4, G, P, T, 32, 951, 1C4*, 1K4*
34CD3	12FX	
34CE3	12GK	
34CM3	9HP	
34DK3	9SG	
34GD5	7CV	34GD5A, 32ET5, A
34GD5A	7CV	32ET5A, 34GD5†, 32ET5†
34R3	9CB	
35	5E	35S, 35/51, 35S/51S, 51, 51S, 24A§, 24S§

Tube Type	Basing	Replacement
35/51	5E	35, 35S/51S, 51, 35S, 51S, 24A§, 24S§
35A3	7ET	35C3
35A5	6AA	35A5LT
35A5LT	6AA	35A5
35B5	7BZ	
35C3	7ET	35A3
35C5	7CV	35C5A, 30A5
35C5A	7CV	35C5†, 30A5†
35CD6GA	5BT	
35D5	9FU	
35DZ8	9JE	
35EH5	7CV	35EH5A
35EH5A	7CV	35EH5†
35FN5	8GD	
35GL6	7FZ	
35HB8	9ME	
35L6G	7AC	35L6GT, GT/G
35L6GT	7AC	35L6G, GT/G
35L6GT/G	7AC	35L6G, T
35LR6	12FY	
35S	5E	35S/51S, 51S, 35/51, 35, 51, 24A§, 24S§
35S/51S	5E	35S, 51S, 35/51, 35, 51, 24A§, 24S§
35W4	5BQ	35W4A
35W4A	5BQ	35W4†
35Y4	5AL	
35Z3	4Z	35Z3LT
35Z3LT	4Z	35Z3
35Z4	5AA	35Z4GT
35Z4GT	5AA	35Z4
35Z5	6AD	35Z5G, GT, GT/G
35Z5G	6AD	35Z5, GT, GT/G
35Z5GT	6AD	35Z5, G, GT/G
35Z5GT/G	6AD	35Z5, G, GT
35Z6G	6AD	35Z6GT
35Z6GT	6AD	35Z5
36	5E	36A, 64*, 64A*
36A	5E	36, 64*, 64A*
36AM3	5BQ	36AM3A, B
36AM3A	5BQ	36AM3, B
36AM3B	5BQ	36AM3†, A†
36KD6	12GW	40KD6†
36MC6	9QL	
37	5A	37A, 76, 56A*, 56AS*, 67*, 67A*
37A	5A	37, 76, 56A*, 56AS*, 67*, 67A*
38	5F	38A
38A	5F	38
38A3	9BM	
38HE7	12FS	
38HK7	12FS	38HE7

Tube Type	Basing	Replacement	Tube Type	Basing	Replacement
39	5F	39/44, 44	50FK5	7CV	
39/44	5F	39, 44	50FY8	9EX	
40	4D		50GY7	12FN	50GY7A
40A1	8ES		50GY7A	12FN	
40B2	8ES		50HC6	7FZ	
40FR5	7CV		50HK6	7FZ	50HC6
40KD6	12GW		50HN5	9QW	
40KG6	9RJ		50JY6	8MG	
40Z5	6AD	40Z5GT, 40Z5/45Z5GT, 45Z5GT	50L6G	7AC	50L6GT
			50L6GT	7AC	50L6G
40Z5/45Z5GT	6AD	40Z5, 40Z5GT, 45Z5GT	50X6	7DX	
			50Y6G	7Q	50Y6GT, GT/G
40Z5GT	6AD	40Z5, 40Z5/45Z5GT, 45Z5GT	50Y6GT	7Q	50Y6G, GT/G
			50Y6GT/G	7Q	50Y6G, GT
41	6B	42*	50Y7GT	8AN	50Z7G, GT
42	6B	41*	50Z6G	7Q	50AX6G, GT
42KN6	12GU		50Z7G	8AN	50Z7GT, 50Y7GT
43	6B	43MG	50Z7GT	8AN	50Z7G, 50Y7GT
43MG	6B	43	51	5E	51S, 35, 35/51, 35S/51S, 35S, 24A§, 24S§
44	5F	39, 39/44			
45	4D	45A			
45A	4D	45	51S	5E	51, 35, 35/51, 35S/51S, 35S, 24A§, 24S§
45A5	8GW				
45B5	9CV				
45Z3	5AM		52	5C	
45Z5GT	6AD	40Z5, 40Z5/45Z5GT, 40Z5GT	53	7B	
			53HK7	12FS	58HE7
46	5C		55	6G	55S
47	5B		55N3	9BM	
48	6A		55S	6G	55
49	5C		56	5A	56S, 27, S
50	4D		56A	5A	56AS, 67, A, 37*, A*, 76*
50A1	9CM				
50A5	6AA		56AS	5A	56A, 67, A, 37*, A*, 76*
50AX6G	7Q	50AX6GT			
50AX6GT	7Q	50AX6G	56R9	12EN	
50B5	7BZ		56S	5A	56, 27, S
50BK5	9BQ		57	6F	57S
50BM8	9EX		57A	6F	57AS, 6C6*, 77*
50C5	7CV	50C5A	57AS	6F	57A, 6C6*, 77*
50C5A	7CV	50C5†	57S	6F	57
50C6G	7AC	50C6GA	58	6F	58S
50C6GA	7S	50C6G	58AS	6F	6D6*, 78*
50CA5	7CV	50EH5, 50EH5A	58HE7	12FS	
50CD6G	5BT		58S	6F	58
50DC4	5BQ		59	7A	
50E5	8GT		60E3	7ET	
50EH5	7CV	50EH5A, 50CA5	60EH5	7CV	
50EH5A	7CV	50EH5†, 50CA5†	60FX5	7CV	
50FA5	7CV		60HL5	9QW	
50FE5	8KB		64	5E	64A, 65, A, 36*, A*
			64A	5E	64, 65, A, 36*, A*

§ May not work in all circuits.   * Parallel-filament circuits.
† Series circuit not requiring controlled warm-up time.

Tube Type	Basing	Replacement
65	5E	65A, 64, A
65A	5E	65, 64, A
67	5A	67A, 56A, AS, 37*, A*, 76*
67A	5A	67, 56A, AS, 37*, A*, 76*
68	5E	68A
68A	5E	68
70A7GT	8AB	
70L7GT	8AA	
71	4D	71A*, B*
71A	4D	71*, B*
71B	4D	71*, A*
75	6G	75S
75S	6G	75
VR75	4AJ	OA3, A
76	5A	37, A, 56A*, AS*, 67*, A*
77	6F	6C6, 57A*, AS*
78	6F	6D6, 58AS
79	6H	
80	4C	5X3, 13, 83V, 88
81	4B	16, B
82	4C	82V
82V	4C	82
83	4C	5Z3
83V	4AD	
84/6Z4	5D	6Z4, 98
G84	4B	2Z2, 2Z2/G84
85	6G	85S
85AS	6G	
85S	6G	85
88	4C	82, 82V
89	6F	89Y
89Y	6F	89
VR90	4AJ	OB3, A
95	6B	2A5
96	4G	
98	5D	84/6Z4, 6Z4
V99	4E	
X99	4D	
VR105	4AJ	OC3, A
112A	4D	12A
117L7GT	8AO	117L7/M7GT, 117M7GT
117L7/M7GT	8AO	117L7GT, M7GT
117M7GT	8AO	117L7GT, L7/M7GT
117N7GT	8AV	117P7GT
117P7GT	8AV	117N7GT
117Z3	4CB	
117Z4GT	5AA	
117Z6GT	7Q	117Z6G, GT/G
117Z6GT/G	7Q	117Z6G, GT

Tube Type	Basing	Replacement
VR150	4AJ	OD3, A
182B/482B	4D	71*, A*, B*
183/483	4D	
485	5A	
807	5AW	
950	5K	
951	4K	1A4, P, T, 1B4P, G, T, 32, 34, 1C4*, 1K4*
5879	9AD	
5881	7AC	6L6GC, 7581, A
6080	8BD	6AS7G, GA, GT
6267	9CQ	
6550	7S	
6973	9EU	
7025	9A	7025A, 12AX7, A, 12DF7, 12DT7, 12AD7*, 12BZ7*, 12DM7*
7025A	9A	7025, 12AX7, A, 12DF7, 12DT7, 12AD7*, 12BZ7*, 12DM7*
7027	8HY	7027A
7189	9CV	7189A
7189A	9LE	
7199	9JT	
7247	9A	12DW7
7355	8KN	
7408	7AC	6V6, G, GT, GTA, GT/G, GTY, GTX
7534	8KE	
7543	7BK	6AU6, A
7581	7AC	7581A, 6L6GC
7581A	7AC	
7591	8KQ	7591A
7591A	8KQ	
7687	9AE	
7695	9MQ	
7754	9MQ	
7867	5BT	6EX6*
7868	9RW	
8278	9QB	
9001	7BD	
9002	7BS	
9003	7BD	
XXB	7BW	3C6
XXD	8AC	14AF7
XXFM	8BZ	7X7
XXL	5AC	7A4
X155	9AJ	6BC8, 6BQ7, A, 6BS8, 6BZ7, 6BZ8, 6BK7*, A*, B*

Picture-Tube Substitutes

This listing is numerical-alphabetical, with the substitutes shown in the right-hand column. Substitutes are not recommended for some types and for this reason are not shown in many instances. The listing of a certain tube type as a substitute for another one does not necessarily mean the reverse is true. Always refer to the left-hand column for the original type number, then find the substitute in the right-hand column.

Minor changes may be necessary when a picture tube is substituted. These changes are indicated by various symbols following the type number. The key to these symbols is given below. *Be absolutely certain* to refer to this key.

The basing code is given in the second column. Use this number and refer to Section 7 for the pin connections.

A listing of those tubes that require odd filament voltages (other than 6.3 volts) is given on page 69. Those tubes having low E_{g2} potentials are listed on pages 68 and 69. This is a handy reference when setting up your picture-tube testing and rejuvenating equipment.

Key to Footnotes:

* Omit ion trap.
** Add ion trap.
† May require longer or shorter H.V. lead.
‡ Connect pin 6 to pin 2 or pin 10.
[1] Parallel-filament circuits only.
[2] In some cases it may be necessary to reverse the red and green cathode leads to achieve proper balance.
[6] Add high-voltage filter capacitor.
[7] Ground the aquadag coating.
[8] Change the anode connector.
[9] Change the ion trap.

Tube Type	Basing	Replacement
1VABP4		
1VACP4		
2EP4	8JK	
3VABP4	7GR	
5VABP4	7GR	
5VACPR	7GR	
5VADP4	7GR	
7RP4	12D	7RP4A
7RP4A	12D	7RP4
8AP4	12H	8AP4A
8AP4A	12H	8AP4
8HP4	12L	8MP4
8LP4	7FA	
8MP4	12L	
9ACP4	7GR	9AGP4, 9WP4
9ADP4	8HR	
9AEP4	7GR	
9AGP4	7GR	9ACP4
9QP4	12AD	9QP4A
9QP4A	12AD	9QP4
9SP4	8HR	
9TP4	8HR	
9UP4	7GR	9VP4/230DB4, 9YP4
9VABP4	7GR	
9VACP22	14BL	
9VADP4	7GR	
9VAEP4	7GR	
9VAGP4	7GR	
9VAHP4	7GR	
9VAJP4	7GR	9VAWP4
9VAKP4	7GR	9VALP4, 9VASP4
9VALP4	7GR	9VASP4
9VAMP4	7GR	
9VANP4	7GR	
9VARP4	7GR	
9VASP4	7GR	9VALP4, 9VAUP4
9VATP4	7GR	
9VAUP4	7GR	9VALP4, 9VASP4
9VAWP4	7GR	9VAJP4
9VAZP4	7GR	
9VP4	7GR	9YP4
9WP4	7GR	
9XP4		
9YP4	7GR	
10ABP4	12L	10ABP4A, B, C, 10AEP4[1]
10ABP4A	12L	10ABP4, B, C, 10AEP4[1]
10ABP4B	12L	10ABP4, A, C, 10AEP4[1]
10ABP4C	12L	10ABP4, A, B, 10AEP4[1]
10ADP4	12L	
10AEP4	12L	10ABP4[1], A[1], B[1], C[1]
10AJP4	12S	
10ARP4	7GR	
10ASP4	7GR	9AEP4, 9VABP4
10ATP4	7GR	
10AVP4	7GR	9VAHP4
10BP4	12N	10BP4A, C[9], D[9], 10FP4*, 10FP4A*
10BP4A	12N	10BP4, C[9], D[9], 10FP4*, A*
10BP4C	12N	10BP4D, 10BP4[9], A[9], 10FP4*, A*
10BP4D	12N	10BP4C, 10BP4[9], A[9], 10FP4*, A*
10CP4	12N	
10DP4	12M	
10EP4	12N	10BP4A[8], 10CP4*, 10FP4*[8], A*[8]
10FP4	12N	10FP4A, 10BP4**, A**, C**, D**
10FP4A	12N	10FP4, 10BP4**, A**, C**, D**
10MP4	12G	10MP4A
10MP4A	12G	10MP4
10RP4	12L	
10VABP22	14BM	
10VACP4	7GR	
10VADP22	14BM	
10VAEP4	7GR	
10VAFP4	7GR	
10VAGP4	7GR	
10VAHP22	14BP	
11AP4	8HR	11HP4
11BP4	8HR	11HP4
11CP4	8HR	11LP4[1]
11DP4	8HR	
11EP4	8HR	11FP4[1]
11FP4	8HR	11EP4[1]
11GP4	8HR	11MP4[1]
11HP4	8HR	11HP4A
11HP4A	8HR	11HP4
11JP4	8HR	
11KP4	8HR	
11LP4	8HR	11CP4[1]
11MP4	8HR	7RP4A
11QP4	7GR	280NB4
11RP4	7GR	11UP4
11SP22	14BJ	11WP22
11TP4	8HR	
11UP4	7GR	11RP4
11WP22	14BJ	
12AYP4	8HR	12AZP4[1], 12BAP4[1], 12BSP4[1]
12AZP4	8HR	12AYP4[1], 12BAP4[1], 12BSP4[1]

Tube Type	Basing	Replacement	Type	Basing	Tube Replacement
12BAP4	8HR	12BSP4, 12AYP4[1], 12AZP4[1]	12DGP4A	7GR	
12BEP4	(7FA) 7EA or 7FB ?		12DHP4	8HR	12BKP4, 12BLP4†, A†, 12BQP4†,
12BFP4	7GR				12BUP4†, A†,
12BGP4	8HR				12VABP4
12BJP4	8HR		12DKP4	7GR	
12BKP4	8HR	12BLP4A, 12BQP4,	12DMP4	8HR	
		12DHP4†,	12DQP4	8HR	12BKP4, 12DHP4,
		12DQP4†,			12VABP4†
		12VABP4†	12DSP4	7GR	
12BKP4A	8HR		12JP4	12D	12RP4**, 12QP4**,
12BLP4	8HR	12BKP4, 12BQP4,			12QP4A**
		12DHP4†	12KP4	12N	12KP4A, 12ZP4**,
12BMP4	7GR	12CDP4, A			12ZP4A**
12BNP4	8HR	12BNP4A	12KP4A	12N	12KP4, 12ZP4**,
12BNP4A	8HR	12BNP4			12ZP4A**
12BQP4	8HR	12BKP4, 12BLP4,	12LP4	12N	12LP4A, 12LP4C,
		12DHP4†			12KP4*, 12KP4A*,
12BRP4	9RS				12ZP4[9], 12ZP4A[9]
12BSP4	8HR	12AYP4, 12AZP4,	12LP4A	12N	12LP4, 12LP4C,
		12BAP4			12KP4*, 12KP4A*,
12BTP4	8HR				12ZP4[9], 12ZP4A[9]
12BUP4	8HR	12BUP4A, B, 12DQP4	12LP4C	12N	12LP4, 12LP4A,
12BUP4A	8HR	12BUP4, B, C,			12KP*, 12KP4A*,
		12DHP4, 12DQP4			12ZP4[9], 12ZP4A[9]
12BUP4B	8HR	12BUP4, A, C, 12DHP4	12QP4	12D	12QP4A, 12RP4,
12BUP4C	8HR	12BKP4			12JP4*
12BVP4	7GR		12QP4A	12D	12QP4, 12RP4,
12BWP4	8HR				12JP4*
12BZP4	7GR		12RP4	12D	12QP4, 12QP4A,
12CBP4	7FA				12JP4*
12CDP4	7GR	12BMP4	12TP4	12D	
12CDP4A	7GR	12BMP4, 12CDP4	12UP4	12D	12UP4A, 12UP4B[9]
12CEP4	7GR		12UP4A	12D	12UP4, 12UP4B[9]
12CFP4	7GR	12CNP4, A	12UP4B	12D	12UP4[9], 12UP4A[9]
12CHP4	7GR	310BYB4B	12VABP4	8HR	12BKP4†, 12DHP4,
12CNP4	7GR	12CNP4A, 12CFP4,			12DQP4†
		12VAGP4[1]	12VACP4	7GR	
12CNP4A	7GR	12CNP4, 12CFP4,	12VAEP4	7GR	
		12VAGP4[1]	12VAFP4	7GR	
12CQP4	8HR	12BKP4	12VAGP4	7GR	
12CSP4	7GR		12VAHP22	14BH	12VALP22, 12VASP22,
12CTP4	7GR	12DFP4			12VATP22
12CTP4A	7GR		12VAJP22	14BH	
12CUP4	8HR		12VALP22	14BH	12VAHP22,
12CVP4	7GR				12VASP22,
12CWP4	7GR	12CWP4A			12VATP22
12CWP4A	7GR	12CWP4	12VAMP4	7GR	12VAFP4, 12VAWP4
12DCP22	14BH	310FGP22	12VANP4	7GR	
12CXP4	7GR		12VAQP4	7GR	
12CZP4	7GR		12VARP22	14BH	
12DEP4	7GR		12VASP22	14BH	12VALP22,
12DFP4	7GR	12DSP4[1]			12VAHP22,
12DGP4	7GR				12VATP22

Tube Type	Basing	Replacement	Tube Type	Basing	Replacement
12VATP22	14BH	12VAHP22, 12VALP22, 12VASP22	13VANP4	7GR	13VAJP4, 13VAQP4
			13VAQP4	7GR	13VAJP4, 13VANP4
			13VARP4	7GR	13VASP4
12VAUP4	7GR	12VAWP4[1]	13VASP4	7GR	13VARP4
12VAWP4	7GR	12VAFP4, 12VAMP4, 12VAUP4[1]	13VATP22	13R	
			13VAUP22	13M	
12VAXP4	7GR		13VAWP22	14BP	
12VAZP4	7GR		13VAYP22	13L	
12VBDP4	7GR		13VAZP4	7GR	
12VBEP4	7GR		13VBAP22	13K	
12VBFP4	7GR		13VBEP22	13M	
12VBGP4	7GR	12VBFP4	14ACP4	12L	14AEP4*
12VBHP4	7GR		14AEP4	12L	
12VBJP4	7GR		14AJP4	8HR	14ASP4*, 14AVP4*
12VBLP4	7GR		14ARP4	12L	14AUP4[1]
12VBMP4	7GR		14ASP4	8HR	14AVP4
12VBNP4	7GR	12VCGP4	14ATP4	12L	
12VBQP4	7GR	12VCJP4	14AUP4	12L	14AWP4, 14ARP4[1]
12VBRP4	7GR	12VCBP4, 12VCKP4, 12VCLP4	14AVP4	8HR	14ASP4
			14AWP4	12L	14AUP4
12VBWP4	7GR		14BCP22	14AU	
12VBXP4	7GR		14BDP4	12L	
12VBYP4	7GR		14BP4	12N	14BP4A, 14CP4, A, 14EP4, 14CP4B*
12VBZP4	7GR				
12VCAP4	7GR		14BP4A	12N	14BP4, 14CP4, A, 14EP4, 14CP4B*
12VCBP4	7GR	12VBRP4, 12VCLP4	14CP4	12N	14CP4A, 14BP4, A, 14EP4, 14CP4B*
12VCDP4	7GR				
12VCEP4	7GR		14CP4A	12N	14BP4, A, 14CP4, 14EP4, 14CP4B*
12VCFP4	7GR				
12VCGP4	7GR	12VBNP4	14CP4B	12N	14CP4**, A**, 14BP4**, A**, 14EP4**
12VCJP4	7GR	12VBQP4			
12VCKP4	7GR	12VBRP4, 12VCBP4			
12VCLP4	7GR	12VBRP4, 12VCBP4	14DP4	12D	14CP4[7, 9], A[7, 9], 14EP4[7, 9], 14FP4[9], 14UP4*
12VP4	12G	12VP4A			
12VP4A	12G	12VP4			
12WP4	9CH		14EP4	12N	14BP4, A, 14CP4, A, B*
12XP4	12N				
12YP4	12N		14GP4	12L	
12ZP4	12N	12ZP4A, 12JP4[6, 8], 12KP4*, 12KP4A*	14HP4	12L	
			14KP4	12N	14KP4A
12ZP4A	12N	12ZP4, 12JP4[6, 8], 12KP4*, 12KP4A*	14KP4A	12N	
			14NP4	12L	14NP4A, 14RP4, A, 14SP4, 14WP4*, 14XP4[1], A[1], 14ZP4*
13AP4	8HR				
13DP4	8HR				
13GP22	14BH	13MP22	14NP4A	12L	14NP4, 14RP4, A, 14SP4, 14WP4*, 14XP4[1], A[1], 14ZP4*
13JP22	14BH	12VATP22			
13LP22	14BH				
13VAEP22	14BH				
13VAFP22	14BP	13VAGP22	14QP4	12L	14QP4A, B*, 14HP4
13VAGP22	14BP		14QP4A	12L	14QP4, B*, 14HP4
13VAJP4	7GR	13VANP4, 13VAQP4	14QP4B	12L	14QP4**, A**, 14HP4**
13VAKP22	13D				
13VAMP22	13E		14RP4	12L	14RP4A, 14NP4, A, 14SP4, 14WP4*,

Tube Type	Basing	Replacement	Tube Type	Basing	Replacement
		14XP4[1], A[1], 14ZP4*	15VAJP4A	7GR	15VAJP4
14RP4A	12L	14RP4, 14NP4, A, 14SP4, 14WP4*, 14XP4[1], A[1], 14ZP4*	15VALP22	13D	15VAFP22
			15VANP4	7GR	15VANP4A
14SP4	12L	14NP4, A, 14RP4, 14RP4A, 14WP4*, 14XP4[1], 14XP4A[1], 14ZP4*	15VANP4A	7GR	15VANP4
			15WP22	14BH	15LP22
14UP4	12D	14DP4**	15XP22	14BH	
14VADP22	14BH	14VAHP22	15YP22	14BK	
14VAEP22	14BH	14VAGP22, 14VALP22	15ZP22	14BH	
14VAFP22	14BH	14VABP22	16ABP4	12P	16AEP4‡
14VAHP22	14BH	14VADP22	16ACP4	12P	
14VAJP22	14BE		16AEP4	12L	16ABP4
14VAKP22	14BE		16AFP4	12L	
14VALP22	14BH	14VAGP22	16ANP4	8HR	16AQP4, 16ASP4[1], 16AXP4[1]
14VAMP22	14BH				
14VARP4	8HR		16AP4	12D	16AP4A, 16AP4B
14WP4	12L	14ZP4	16AP4A	12D	16AP4, B
14XP4	12L	14XP4A, 14NP4[1], A[1], 14RP4[1], 14RP4A[1], 14SP4[1], 14WP4*[1], 14ZP4*[1]	16AP4B	12D	16AP4, A
			16AQP4	8HR	16ANP4, 16ASP4[1], 16AXP4[1]
			16ASP4	8HR	16AXP4[1], 16ANP4[1], 16AQP4[1]
14XP4A	12L	14XP4, 14NP4[1], A[1], 14RP4[1], 14RP4A[1], 14SP4[1], 14WP4*[1], 14ZP4*[1]	16ATP4	8HR	
			16AUP4	8HR	16BFP4†[1], 16BMP4[1]
			16AVP4	7FA	16BCP4
			16AWP4	8HR	16AZP4[1]
14ZP4	12L	14WP4	16AXP4	8HR	16ASP4, 16ANP4[1], 16AQP4[1]
15ACP22	14BH	14AFP22	16AYP4	8HR	16BDP4[1], 16CAP4
15ADP4	12D		16AZP4	8HR	16AWP4[1]
15AEP22	14BH	14VAGP22, 14VALP22	16BAP4	8HR	16BEP4[1]
15AFP22	14BH	14VAGP22, 14VALP22	16BCP4	7FA	
15AP4	12D	15DP4**, A**	16BDP4	8HR	16AYP4[1]
15CP4	12D		16BEP4	8HR	16BAP4†[1]
15DP4	12D	15DP4A, 15AP4*	16BFP4	8HR	16AUP4†[1], 16BMP4†
15DP4A	12D	15DP4, 15AP4*	16BGP4	8HR	16BWP4, 16BHP4[1], 16BVP4†, 16CAP4, 16CMP4A†
15GP22	20A				
15HP22	20A		16BJP4	8HR	16BGP4[1], 16BWP4[1], 16CMP4A[1]
15JP4	8HR				
15KP22	14BH	15LP22, 15NP22	16BMP4	8HR	16AUP4[1], 16BFP4†
15LP22	14BH	14VADP22, 14VAHP22	16BNP4	8HR	
			16BRP4	8HR	16BVP4[1], 16BWP4[1]†, 16CAP4[1]†, 16CEP4[1]†, 16CJP4[1], 16CKP4[1], 16CMP4[1]
15MP22	14BK				
15NP22	14BH	14VADP22, 14VAHP22			
15RP22	14BH	15LP22	16BSP4	8HR	16BKP4†, 16BLP4†[1], 16BTP4†
15SP22	14BH	14VAGP22, 15AFP22			
15UP22	14BH		16BUP4	8HR	
15VACP4	8HR		16BVP4	8HR	16BWP4†, 16CJP4
15VADP22	13D		16BWP4	8HR	16BGP4, 16BVP4†, 16CAP4, 16CJP4†
15VAEP22	13D				
15VAFP22	13D	15VALP22	16BXP4	7FA	
15VAJP4	7GR	15VAJP4A	16BYP4	8HR	

Tube Type	Basing	Replacement	Tube Type	Basing	Replacement
16CAP4	8HR	16BWP4, 16CEP4, 16BRP4†[1], 16BVP4†, 16CJP4†, 16CKP4[1]†, 16CMP4†	16EP4A	12D	16EP4, 16EP4B
			16EP4B	12D	16EP4, 16EP4A
			16FP4	12D	
			16GP4	12D	16GP4A
16CDP22	14BE		16GP4A	12D	16GP4
16CEP4	8HR	16BWP4, 16CAP4, 16BRP4[1]†, 16BVP4†, 16CJP4†, 16CKP4[1]†, 16CMP4†	16GP4B	12D	16GP4
			16GP4C	12D	16GP4
			16HP4	12N	16HP4A
			16HP4A	12N	16HP4
			16JP4	12N	16JP4A
16CFP4	7GR		16JP4A	12N	16JP4
16CHP4	8HR	16CHP4A, 16BSP4†	16KP4	12N	16KP4A, 16RP4, A, B*, 16TP4
16CHP4A	8HR	16CHP4, 16BSP4†	16KP4A	12N	16KP4, 16RP4, A, B*, 16TP4
16CJP4	8HR	16BWP4†			
16CKP4	8HR	16BRP4[1], 16BVP4[1], 16BWP4[1]†, 16CAP4[1]†, 16CEP4[1]†, 16CJP4[1], 16CMP4[1]	16LP4	12N	16LP4A, 16ZP4
			16LP4A	12N	16LP4, 16ZP4
			16MP4	12N	16MP4A, 16JP4, A
			16MP4A	12N	16MP4, 16JP4, A
			16QP4	12D	16XP4
16CMP4	8HR	16BVP4, 16CJP4, 16BRP4[1], 16BWP4†, 16CAP4†, 16CEP4†, 16CKP4[1]	16RP4	12N	16RP4A, 16KP4, A, 16TP4, 16RP4B*
			16RP4A	12N	16RP4, 16KP4, 16KP4A, 16RP4B*
16CMP4A	8HR	16BGP4†, 16BWP4†	16RP4B	12N	16KP4**, A**, 16RP4**, A**, 16TP4**
16CNP4	7GR				
16CP4	12D		16SP4	12N	16SP4A, 16WP4A, B
16CQP4	7GR		16SP4A	12N	16SP4, 16WP4A, B
16CSP22	14BE	16DAP22, 400CUB22	16TP4	12N	16KP4, A, 16RP4, 16RP4A, 16RP4B*
16CTP4	8HR	16BWP4, 16CAP4, 16CEP4, 16BRP4[1]†, 16BVP4†, 16CJP4†, 16CKP4[1]†, 16CMP4†, 16CUP4†	16UP4	12D	16KP4[7], A[7], 16QP4[9], 16RP4[7], A[7], 16TP4[7], 16XP4[9]
			16VABP4	8HR	16VAQP4, 17EMP4, 17EWP4
16CUP4	8HR	16BVP4, 16CJP4, 16CMP4, 16BRP4[1], 16BWP4†, 16CAP4†, 16CEP4†, 16CKP4[1], 16CTP4†	16VABP22	14BH	16VACP22
			16VACP22	14BH	16VABP22
			16VADP4	7GR	
			16VAFP22	14BH	
			16VAGP4	8HR	
			16VAJP4	8HR	
16CWP4	7GR	16DCP4, A, 16CXP4	16VAKP22	14BH	17FBP22
16CWP4A	7GR		16VALP4	8HR	
16CXP4	7GR	16CWP4, 16DCP4, A	16VAMP22	14BE	
16CYP22	14BH	400CVB22	16VANP22	14BH	
16DAP22	14BE	16CSP22, 400CUB22	16VAQP4	8HR	16VABP4, 16VBNP4, 16VBTP4, 17EWP4, 17FDP4
16DCP4	7GR	16DCP4A, 16CWP4, 16CXP4			
16DCP4A	7GR	16DCP4, 16CWP4, 16CXP4	16VARP4	8HR	
			16VASP22	14BE	16VATP22
16DP4	12D	16DP4A	16VATP22	14BE	16VASP22
16DP4A	12D	16DP4	16VAUP22	14BH	
16EP4	12D	16EP4A, 16EP4B			

Tube Type	Basing	Replacement	Tube Type	Basing	Replacement
16VAWP22	14BK	16VBDP22[1], 16VBMP22[1]	16VCZP4	8HR	
			16VP4	12D	16WP4[9], 16YP4[7]
16VAXP22	14BH		16WP4	12D	16WP4A, B[7], 16SP4[7], A[7], 16VP4[9]
16VAYP4	8HR	16VBCP4A			
16VAZP4	8HR		16WP4A	12N	16WP4B, 16SP4, A, 16WP4[7], 16YP4[9]
16VBCP4	8HR	16VBCP4A, 17ESP4			
16VBCP4A	8HR	16VAYP4, 16VBCP4	16WP4B	12N	16WP4A, 16SP4, A, 16WP4[7], 16YP4[9]
16VBDP22	14BK	16VAWP22[1], 16VBMP22			
			16XP4	12D	16QP4, 16UP4[9]
16VBEP22	14BH		16YP4	12N	16WP4A[9], B[9], 16SP4[9], A[9], 16VP4[6]
16VBFP22	14BE				
16VBGP22	14BE		16ZP4	12N	16LP4, A, 16CP4[6]
16VBHP22	14BE	16VBFP22	17AP4	12N	17BP4B*
16VBJP4	7GR		17ASP4	12N	
16VBKP4	7GR		17ATP4	12L	17ATP4A, 17AVP4, 17AVP4A, 17BUP4, 17CBP4, 17CLP4, 17BJP4*, 17BKP4[1], 17BKP4A[1], 17BSP4*[1], 17CUP4*[1], 17DCP4*[1], 17DJP4[1]
16VBLP4	8HR				
16VBMP22	14BK	16VAWP22[1], 16VBDP22			
16VBNP4	8HR	16VAQP4, 16VBQP4, 16VBTP4, 16VBUP4, 16VBZP4			
			17ATP4A	12L	17ATP4, 17AVP4, A, 17BUP4, 17CBP4, 17CLP4, 17BJP4*, 17BKP4[1], A[1], 17BSP4*[1], 17CUP4*[1], 17DCP4*[1], 17DJP4[1]
16VBQP4	8HR	16VBZP4			
16VBRP4	8HR				
16VBTP4	8HR	16VAQP4, 16VBNP4, 16VBQP4, 16VBUP4, 16VBZP4			
			17AVP4	12L	17AVP4A, 17ATP4, A, 17BUP4, 17CBP4, 17CLP4, 17BJP4*, 17BKP4[1], A[1], 17BSP4*[1], 17CUP4*[1], 17DCP4*[1], 17DJP4[1]
16VBUP4	8HR	16VBNP4, 16VBTP4, 16VBZP4			
16VBWP4	8HR	16VBXP4, 16VBYP4, 16VCXP4			
16VBXP4	8HR	16VBWP4, 16VBYP4, 16VCXP4	17AVP4A	12L	17AVP4, 17ATP4, A, 17BUP4, 17CBP4, 17CLP4, 17BJP4*, 17BKP4[1], A[1], 17BSP4*[1], 17CUP4*[1], 17DCP4*[1], 17DJP4[1]
16VBYP4	8HR	16VBWP4, 16VBXP4, 16VCXP4			
16VBZP4	8HR	16VBQP4			
16VCAP4	7GR				
16VCBP4	7GR		17BJP4	12L	17BSP4[1], 17CUP4[1], 17DCP4[1]
16VCDP4	8HR				
16VCEP4	8HR		17BKP4	12L	17BKP4A, 17ATP4[1], A[1], 17AVP4[1], A[1], 17BJP4*[1], 17BSP4*[1], 17BUP4[1], 17CBP4[1], 17CLP4[1], 17CUP4*[1], 17DCP4*[1], 17DJP4[1]
16VCFP4	8HR				
16VCGP4	8HR				
16VCHP4	8HR				
16VCJP4	8HR				
16VCKP4	8HR	16VCLP4[1]			
16VCLP4	8HR	16VCKP4[1]			
16VCNP4	8HR				
16VCQP4	8HR				
16VCRP4	8HR				
16VCSP4	8HR				
16VCWP4	8HR				
16VCXP4	8HR	16VBWP4, 16VBXP4, 16VBYP4			
16VCYP4	8HR				

Tube Type	Basing	Replacement
17BKP4A	12L	17BKP4, 17ATP4[1], A[1], 17AVP4[1], A[1], 17BJP4*[1], 17BSP4*, 17BUP4[1], 17CBP4[1], 17CLP4[1], 17CUP4*[1], 17DCP4*[1], 17DJP4[1]
17BMP4	12L	17BNP4*
17BNP4	12L	
17BP4	12D	17BP4A[7], 17BP4B[7], 17BP4C[7], 17BP4D[7], 17AP4[7], 17JP4[7]
17BP4A	12N	17BP4[6], B, C, D*, 17AP4, 17JP4
17BP4B	12N	17BP4[6], 17BP4A, 17BP4C, 17BP4D*, 17AP4, 17JP4
17BP4C	12N	17BP4[6], 17BP4A, 17BP4B, 17BP4D*, 17AP4, 17JP4
17BP4D	12N	17BP4**[6], 17BP4A**, 17BP4B**, 17BP4C**, 17AP4**, 17JP4**
17BRP4	8HR	17BZP4*[1], 17CAP4*, 17CKP4*, 17CTP4*[1], 17CVP4*[1], 17DTP4*[1], 17DZP4*[1]
17BSP4	12L	17BJP4[1], 17CUP4[1], 17DCP4[1]
17BTP4	12AJ	
17BUP4	12L	17ATP4, A, 17AVP4, A, 17CBP4, 17CLP4, 17BJP4*, 17BKP4[1], 17BKP4A[1], 17BSP4*[1], 17CUP4*[1], 17DCP4*[1], 17DJP4[1]
17BVP4	7FA	17BWP4*, 17BYP4*[1], 17CSP4*
17BWP4	7FA	17CSP4, 17BYP4[1]
17BYP4	7FA	17BWP4[1], 17CSP4[1]
17BZP4	8HR	17DSP4
17CAP4	8HR	17BZP4, 17CKP4, 17DTP4, 17BRP4**, 17CTP4[1], 17CVP4[1], 17DZP4[1]
17CBP4	12L	17ATP4, A, 17AVP4, A, 17BUP4, 17CLP4, 17BJP4*, 17BKP4[1], A[1], 17BSP4*[1], 17CUP4*[1], 17DCP4*[1], 17DJP4[1]
17CDP4	8HR	
17CEP4	12L	17CFP4[1]
17CFP4	12L	17CEP4[1]
17CGP4	12L	
17CKP4	8HR	17CAP4, 17BRP4**, 17BZP4[1], 17CTP4[1], 17CVP4[1], 17DTP4[1], 17BZP4[1], 17DSP4
17CLP4	12L	17ATP4, A, 17AVP4, A, 17BUP4, 17CBP4, 17BJP4*, 17BKP4[1], A[1], 17BSP4*[1], 17CUP4*[1], 17DCP4*[1], 17DJP4[1]
17CMP4	12L	17CNP4, 17CRP4[1], 17CXP4[1]
17CNP4	12L	17CMP4, 17CRP4[1], 17CXP4[1]
17CP4	12D	17CP4A
17CP4A	12D	17CP4
17CRP4	12L	17CXP4, 17CMP4[1], 17CNP4[1]
17CSP4	7FA	17BWP4, 17BYP4[1]
17CTP4	8HR	17BZP4[1], 17CAP4[1], 17CKP4[1], 17CVP4[1], 17DTP4[1], 17DZP4[1]
17CUP4	12L	17DCP4, 17BJP4, 17BSP4, 17DJP4**
17CVP4	8HR	17BZP4[1], 17CAP4[1], 17CKP4[1], 17CTP4[1], 17DTP4[1], 17DZP4[1]
17CWP4	8HR	17DSP4, 17EFP4[1]
17CXP4	12L	17CRP4, 17CMP4[1], 17CNP4[1]
17CYP4	12L	17BJP4, 17CZP4
17CZP4	12L	17BJP4, 17CYP4
17DAP4	8JK	17DRP4
17DBP4	12L	17DWP4*[1], 17HP4[1], 17HP4A[1], 17HP4B[1], 17HP4C*[1], 17KP4[1], A[1], 17RP4[1], C[1]
17DCP4	12L	17CUP4, 17BJP4[1], 17BSP4[1]
17DEP4	8JN	
17DHP4	8HR	17EBP4
17DJP4	12L	17ATP4[1], A[1], 17AVP4[1], A[1], 17BJP4*[1], 17BKP4[1], A[1], 17BSP4*[1], 17BUP4[1], 17CBP4[1],

Tube Type	Basing	Replacement	Tube Type	Basing	Replacement
		17CLP4[1], 17CUP4*, 17DCP4*	17HP4C	12L	17HP4**, A**, B**, 17DWP4, 17KP4**, A**
17DKP4	8JR	17DSP4	17JP4	12N	17AP4, 17BP4[6], A, B, C, D*
17DLP4	8JS	17DSP4, 17EBP4[1]			
17DQP4	7FA		17KP4	12P	17KP4A
17DRP4	8JK	17DAP4	17KP4A	12P	17KP4
17DSP4	8HR	17EBP4[1], 17EFP4[1]	17LP4	12L	17LP4A, 17VP4, B
17DTP4	8HR	17DKP4, 17DSP4	17LP4A	12L	17LP4, B*, 17VP4, B
17DWP4	12L	17DWP4A	17LP4B	12L	17LP4**, A**, 17VP4**, B**
17DWP4A	12L				
17DXP4	8JR	17DHP4, 17EBP4, 17DKP4[1]	17QCP4	12N	
17DZP4	8HR	17DTP4[1]	17QP4	12N	17QP4A, B*, 17YP4
17EAP4	12AT		17QP4A	12N	17QP4, B*, 17YP4
17EBP4	8HR		17QP4B	12N	17QP4**, A**, 17YP4**
17EFP4	12L	17DXP4			
17EHP4	8HR		17RP4	12L	17RP4C, 17HP4, A, B, C*, 17KP4, A, 17DBP4[1], 17DWP4*
17EJP22	14AU	17ENP22			
17EKP4	12L				
17ELP4	8HR				
17ELP4A	8HR		17RP4C	12L	17RP4, 17HP4, A, B, C*, 17KP4, A, 17DBP4[1], 17DWP4*
17EMP4	8HR	16VABP4, 16VAQP4, 17EWP4			
17ENP22	14AU	17EJP22	17SP4	12N	
17EQP4	8HR	17FCP4	17TP4	12M	
17ESP4	8HR	16VBCP4, A	17UP4	12N	17QP4, 17QP4A, B*, 17YP4
17ETP22	14BE				
17EVP22	14BH	16VAFP22	17VACP22	14BH	17VADP22
17EWP4	8HR	16VABP4, 17EMP4	17VADP22	14BE	
17EXP22	14BK	17FJP22	17VAKP22	14BE	
17EZP22	14BH	16VABP22, 16VACP22	17VANP22	13D	17VAYP22
17FAP22	14BE		17VAQP22	14BP	17VAXP22
17FBP22	14BH	16VAKP22	17VARP22	14BE	
17FCP4	8HR	17EQP4	17VASP22	14BE	
17FDP4	8HR	16VAQP4	17VATP22	13D	17VAZP22
17FEP22	14BH	16VACP22	17VAUP22	14BE	17VARP22
17FGP22	14BH	16VACP22	17VAWP22	14BH	
17FHP22	14BH		17VAXP22	14BP	
17FJP22	14BK	17EXP22	17VAYP22	13D	17VANP22
17FP4	12L	17FP4A, 17HP4C*	17VAZP22	13D	17VATP22
17FP4A	12L	17FP4, 17HP4C*	17VBDP22	13E	
17GP4	12M		17VBLP22	13M	
17HP4	12L	17HP4A, B, C*, 17KP4, A, 17RP4, C, 17DBP4[1], 17DWP4*	17VBMP22	13L	
			17VBNP22	13K	
			17VBTP22	13L	
			18VARP22	14BE	
17HP4A	12L	17HP4, B, C*, 17KP4, A, 17RP4, C, 17DBP4[1], 17DWP4*	17VP4	12L	17VP4B, 17LP4, A, B*
			17VP4B	12L	17VP4, 17LP4, A, B*
			17YP4	12N	17QP4, A, B*
17HP4B	12L	17HP4, A, C*, 17KP4, A, 17RP4, C, 17DBP4[1], 17DWP4*	18VABP22	14BE	18VAJP22, 18VASP22, 18VATP22
			18VAHP22	14BE	
			18VAJP22	14BE	18VAHP22, 18VASP22, 18VATP22,

Tube Type	Basing	Replacement
		18VBHP22, 18VBKP22, 18VBTP22
18VAKP22	14BE	
18VALP22	14BH	18VAHP22, 18VATP22, 18VBGP22, 18VBKP22, 19JSP22
18VAMP22	14BH	18VBDP22
18VANP22	13C	
18VASP22	14BE	18VAJP22, 18VBKP22
18VATP22	14BE	18VAJP22, 18VBTP22
18VAZP22	14BH	
18VBCP22	14BE	19HFP22
18VBDP22	14BH	18VAMP22, 18VBGP22
18VBEP22	14BE	
18VBFP22	14BE	18VAKP22
18VBGP22	14BH	18VALP22, 19JSP22
18VBHP22	14BE	18VAJP22, 18VASP22, 18VBKP22[1], 19HXP22
18VBJP22	14BE	
18VBKP22	14BE	18VAJP22, 18VASP22
18VBMP22	14BE	
18VBQP4	8HR	
18VBTP22	14BE	18VAJP22, 18VATP22, 19HCP22, 19JZP22
18VBUP22	14BH	
18VBXP22	14BE	
19ABP4	8JK	
19ACP4	8HR	19CHP4, 19CKP4, 19DLP4, 19FVP4†[1]
19AEP4	8HR	
19AFP4	8HR	19AUP4, 19BAP4[1], 19BCP4[1]
19AHP4	8HR	19ALP4[1], 19AYP4
19AJP4	7FA	19CDP4[1], 19CQP4[1], 19CXP4[1]
19ALP4	8HR	19AHP4[1]
19ANP4	8JR	19AYP4, 19YP4[1]
19AP4	12D	19AP4A, B, C, D
19AP4A	12D	19AP4, B, C, D
19AP4B	12D	19AP4, A, C, D
19AP4C	12D	19AP4, A, B, D
19AP4D	12D	19AP4, A, B, C
19AQP4	8HR	19AXP4[1], 19BLP4[1], 19XP4[1]
19ARP4	8HR	19ASP4[1], 19CEP4[1]
19ASP4	8HR	19CEP4, 19ARP4[1]
19ATP4	8JR	19AFP4, 19AUP4,

Tube Type	Basing	Replacement
		19BAP4[1], 19BCP4[1], 19BMP4[1]
19AUP4	8HR	19AFP4, 19BAP4[1], 19BCP4[1]
19AVP4	8HR	19AYP4[1]
19AXP4	8HR	19AYP4, 19AVP4[1], 19XP4[1]
19AYP4	8HR	19AVP4[1]
19BAP4	8HR	19BCP4, 19AFP4[1], 19AUP4[1]
19BCP4	8HR	19BAP4, 19AFP4[1], 19AUP4[1]
19BDP4	12L	
19BEP4	8HR	19CTP4, 19DJP4, 19BSP4[1]
19BFP4	12L	
19BHP4	8HR	19AVP4
19BLP4	8HR	19AVP4, 19CYP4
19BMP4	8HR	19AFP4, 19AUP4, 19BAP4[1], 19BCP4[1]
19BNP4	8HR	19BQP4, 19CVP4[1], 19DYP4[1], 19GMP4[1]
19BQP4	8HR	19BNP4, 19CVP4[1], 19DYP4[1], 19GMP4[1]
19BRP4	8HR	19DKP4, 19CZP4[1], 19DAP4[1], 19DEP4
19BSP4	8HR	19AVP4, 19BEP4[1], 19CTP4[1], 19DJP4[1]
19BTP4	8JR	19AVP4, 19CYP4
19BVP4	8HR	19AVP4, 19BWP4[1]
19BWP4	8HR	19AYP4, 19BVP4[1]
19CAP4	8JR	19AVP4, 19BTP4
19CDP4	7FA	19CQP4, 19CXP4, 19AJP4[1]
19CEP4	8HR	19BAP4, 19BCP4, 19AFP4[1], 19AUP4[1], 19BMP4[1]
19CFP4	8HR	19CHP4, 19CKP4, 19DLP4, 19FVP4†[1]
19CGP4	12L	
19CHP4	8HR	19CKP4, 19DLP4, 19FVP4†[1]
19CJP4	8HR	19AVP4
19CKP4	8HR	19CHP4, 19FVP4†[1]
19CLP4	12L	19BDP4, 19CRP4
19CMP4	8HR	19CMP4A, 19CHP4[1]
19CMP4A	8HR	19CUP4
19CQP4	7FA	19CDP4, 19CXP4, 19AJP4[1]
19CUP4	8HR	19DFP4[1]
19CVP4	8HR	19DYP4, 19GMP4
19CXP4	7FA	19CDP4, 19CQP4, 19AJP4[1]
19CYP4	8HR	19AVP4

Tube Type	Basing	Replacement
19CZP4	8HR	19DAP4, 19DKP4[1]
19DAP4	8HR	19CZP4, 19DKP4[1]
19DBP4	7FA	
19DCP4	8HR	19EDP4, 19EUP4, 19DWP4[1], 19FCP4[1], 19FTP4[1], 19GJP4[1], A[1]
19DEP4	8HR	19AVP4
19DFP4	8HR	19CHP4, 19CUP4[1]
19DHP4	8HR	19DSP4, 19EFP4, 19ESP4, 19DUP4[1], 19EAP4[1], 19ENP4[1], A[1], 19FUP4†[1]
19DJP4	8HR	19BEP4, 19BSP4
19DKP4	8HR	19CZP4[1], 19DAP4[1]
19DLP4	8HR	19CHP4, 19CKP4, 19EDP4
19DNP4	8HR	19DKP4[1], 19CZP4[1], 19DAP4[1], 19EDP4
19DP4	12N	19DP4A, 19FP4[6, 9], 19GP4[6]
19DP4A	12N	19DP4, 19FP4[6, 9], 19GP4[6]
19DQP4	8HR	19DRP4[1], 19FLP4†, 19FRP4[1]
19DRP4	8HR	19DQP4[1], 19FLP4†[1], 19FRP4[1]
19DSP4	8HR	19DHP4, 19EFP4, 19ESP4, 19DUP4[1], 19EAP4[1], 19ENP4[1], A[1], 19FUP4†[1]
19DUP4	8HR	19ENP4, A, 19GHP4
19DVP4	8HR	19DZP4
19DWP4	8HR	19EVP4, 19FCP4, 19GJP4, A, 19EDP4[1]
19DYP4	8HR	19CVP4, 19GMP4
19DZP4	8HR	19BVP4, 19DVP4
19EAP4	8HR	19DUP4, 19ENP4, A, 19DHP4[1], 19DSP4[1], 19EFP4[1], 19ESP4[1]
19EBP4	8HR	19GFP4†[1]
19ECP4	8HR	19FTP4, 19HGP4†
19EDP4	8HR	19DWP4[1], 19FCP4[1], 19GJP4[1], A[1]
19EFP4	8HR	19DHP4, 19DSP4, 19ESP4, 19DUP4[1], 19EAP4[1], 19ENP4[1], A[1], 19GHP4
19EGP4	8HR	19HAP4[1]
19EHP4	8HR	19EHP4A, 19DCP4, 19FJP4[1]
19EHP4A	8HR	19EHP4, 19DCP4, 19FJP4[1]
19EJP4	8HR	19FEP4, A, B
19EKP4	8HR	19EZP4
19ELP4	8HR	19AVP4
19ENP4	8HR	19ENP4A, 19DUP4, 19EAP4, 19DHP4[1], 19DSP4[1], 19EFP4[1], 19ESP4[1], 19GHP4
19ENP4A	8HR	19ENP4, 19DUP4, 19EAP4, 19DHP4[1], 19DSP4[1], 19EFP4[1], 19ESP4[1], 19GHP4
19EP4	12D	19JP4
19ESP4	8HR	19DHP4, 19DSP4, 19EFP4, 19DUP4[1], 19EAP4[1], 19ENP4[1], A[1], 19GHP4
19ETP4	8HR	
19EUP4	8HR	19DWP4[1], 19EDP4, 19FCP4[1], 19FTP4[1], 19GJP4[1], A[1]
19EXP22	14BE	18VAHP22, 19GVP22, 19GYP22
19EYP22	14BE	18VAHP22, 19FMP22
19EZP4	7FA	19EKP4
19FAP4	8HR	
19FBP4	8HR	19EGP4, 19HAP4[1]
19FCP4	8HR	19DWP4, 19GJP4, A, 19EDP4[1]
19FEP4	8HR	19FEP4A, B, 19EJP4
19FEP4A	8HR	19FEP4B
19FEP4B	8HR	19FEP4A
19FGP4	8JR	19EBP4
19FHP4	8HR	
19FJP4	8HR	19DCP4[1], 19EHP4[1], 19EHP4A[1]
19FJP4A	8HR	19DWP4, 19EDP4[1], 19FCP4, 19GJP4, A, 19GRP4
19FLP4	8HR	19DQP4†, 19DRP4†[1], 19FRP4†[1], 19FTP4
19FNP4	8HR	19GEP4[1], 19GKP4[1]
19FP4	12D	19GP4
19FQP4	8HR	
19FRP4	8HR	19DQP4[1], 19DRP4[1], 19FLP4†[1]
19FSP4	8HR	
19FTP4	8HR	18VBQP4, 19DWP4, 19FCP4, 19GJP4, A, 19DCP4[1], 19EDP4[1], 19EUP4[1], 19FTP4A
19FTP4A	8HR	18VBQP4, 19DCP4[1], 19DWP4, 19EDP4,

Tube Type	Basing	Replacement	Tube Type	Basing	Replacement
		19EUP4, 19FCP4, 19GJP4, A	19HTP22	14BH	18VBJP22
19FWP4	8HR		19HXP22	14BE	18VAJP22, 18VASP22, 18VBHP22
19FXP22	14BE	18VAHP22, 19GWP22	19HYP22	14BH	18VAMP22, 18VBDP22
19FZP4	8HR		19JAP22	14BH	
19GAP4	8HR		19JBP22	14BE	
19GBP4	8HR	19CZP4, 19DAP4, 19DKP4[1]	19JCP22	14BH	
			19JLP22	14BE	
19GDP22	14BE	19GZP22	19JNP22	14BE	18VABP22, 18VAJP22, 18VAMP22
19GEP4	8HR	19FNP4[1], 19GEP4A			
19GEP4A	8HR	19FNP4[1], 19GEP4			
19GFP4	8HR	19EBP4†[1]	19JVP22	14BH	
19GHP4	8HR	19DHP4[1], 19DSP4[1], 19DUP4, 19EAP4, 19EFP4[1], 19ENP4, A, 19ESP4[1]	19JP4	12D	19EP4
			19JSP22	14BH	18VALP22, 18VBGP22
			19JWP22	14BH	
19GJP4	8HR	19GJP4A, 19DWP4, 19EDP4[1], 19FCP4	19JYP22	14BE	18VAHP22
			19JZP22	14BE	18VAJP22, 18VATP22, 18VBTP22
19GJP4A	8HR	19GJP4, 19DWP4, 19EDP4[1], 19FCP4			
19GKP4	8HR	19FNP4[1], 19GEP4[1]	19KAP22	14BE	
19GLP22	14BE	18VAHP22[1]	19KLP22	14BE	18VAKP22
19GMP4	8HR	19CVP4, 19DYP4	19QP4	12L	
19GQP4	8HR		19TP22	20A	
19GP4	12D	19FP4[9]	19VADP22	13C	
19GSP22	14BE	18VAHP22[1], 19EYP22	19VAFP22	14BE	19VEDP22
19GTP4	8HR		19VAGP22	14BE	19VAFP22
19GVP22	14BE	18VAHP22[2], 19GYP22	19VAHP4	8HR	19VBXP4, 19VCJP4, 19VCLP4, 19VCMP4, 19VGXP4, 19VHGP4
19GWP22	14BE	18VAHP22, 19HBP22, 19HRP22, 19JYP22			
19GYP22	14BE	19EXP22, 19GVP22, 19HQP22	19VAJP4	8HR	
			19VAKP22	14BE	
19GZP22	14BE	19GDP22	19VALP4	8HR	
19HAP4	8HR	19EGP4[1]	19VAMP22	14BE	
19HBP22	14BE	18VAHP22, 19GWP22, 19HRP22, 19JYP22	19VANP22	14BH	19VBQP22
			19VAQP22	14BE	19VBSP22, 19VCBP22, 19VCSP22, 19VDMP22, 19VDUP22, 19VEFP22, 19VEGP22
19HCP22	14BE	18VAJP22, 18VASP22, 18VATP22, 18VBTP22, 19JZP22			
19HFP22	14BE	18VBCP22	19VARP4	8HR	19VDHP4, 19VENP4
19HGP4	8HR	19ECP4†	19VASP4	8HR	
19HJP22	14BE	18VABP22	19VATP22	14BE	19VBRP22, 19VBWP22, 19VCFP22, 19VCTP22, 19VCYP22, 19VDQP22, 19VDTP22, 19VDXP22, 19VEAP22, 19VEDP22,
19HMP22	14BE	18VBMP22			
19HNP22	14BH	18VAZP22			
19HRP22	14BE	18VAHP22, 19GWP22, 19HBP22, 19JYP22			
19HQP22	14BE	18VAHP22, 19GYP22			
19HSP22	14BH				

Tube Type	Basing	Replacement
		19VEUP22, 19VHJP22
19VAUP22	14BE	19VCFP22
19VAWP22	14BE	
19VAXP22	14BE	19VBJP22
19VAYP22	14BH	
19VAZP22	14BH	
19VBAP22	14BE	
19VBCP22	14BH	
19VBDP22	14BE	
19VBFP22	14BE	
19VBGP22	14BE	
19VBHP22	14BH	
19VBJP22	14BE	19VAXP22
19VBLP22	13C	
19VBNP4	8HR	19VEMP4, 20AHP4
19VBNP4A	8HR	19VEMP4, 20AHP4
19VBQP22	14BH	
19VBRP22	14BE	19VCFP22, 19VCNP22, 19VCTP22, 19VCXP22, 19VDFP22, 19VDQP22, 19VDYP22, 19VEAP22, 19VEDP22, 19VHJP22
19VBSP22	14BE	19VAQP22, 19VCBP22, 19VCSP22, 19VDMP22, 19VDUP22, 19VEFP22, 19VEGP22
19VBWP22	14BE	19VATP22[1], 19VBRP22[1], 19VCRP22, 19VCTP22[1], 19VDFP22[1], 19VDQP22[1], 19VEAP22[1], 19VEBP22[1]
19VBXP4	8HR	19VAHP4, 19VCGP4, 19VCJP4, 19VCLP4, 19VCMP4
19VBYP4	8HR	
19VBZP4	8HR	19VCMP4, 19VDGP4
19VCAP22	14BH	19VANP22
19VCBP22	14BE	19VCSP22, 19VDMP22, 19VEFP22, 19VEGP22
19VCFP22	14BE	19VATP22,

Tube Type	Basing	Replacement
		19VAUP22, 19VBRP22, 19VCNP22, 19VCTP22, 19VCXP22, 19VCYP22, 19VDSP22, 19VDWP22, 19VDYP22
19VCGP4	8HR	19VAHP4, 19VBXP4, 19VCJP4, 19VCLP4, 19VCMP4
19VCHP4	8HR	
19VCJP4	8HR	19VAHP4, 19VBXP4, 19VCJP4, 19VCLP4, 19VCMP4
19VCKP4	8HR	19VEDP4, 20XP4
19VCLP4	8HR	19VBXP4, 19VCGP4, 19VCJP4, 19VCMP4, 20YP4, 20ZP4
19VCMP4	8HR	19VBXP4, 19VCGP4, 19VCJP4, 19VCLP4, 20ABP4, 20YP4, 20ZP4
19VCNP22	14BE	19VBRP22, 19VCFP22, 19VDYP22
19VCQP22A	14BE	19VAFP22, 19VDZP22
19VCRP22	14BE	19VDQP22[1], 19VEAP22[1], 19VEDP22[1]
19VCSP22	14BE	19VAQP22, 19VCBP22, 19VDMP22, 19VDUP22, 19VEFP22, 19VEGP22
19VCTP22	14BE	19VBRP22, 19VCFP22, 19VDFP22, 19VDQP22, 19VDSP22, 19VEAP22, 19VEDP22, 19VHBP22, 19VHJP22
19VCUP4	8HR	19VARP4
19VCWP22	13C	
19VCXP22	14BE	19VBRP22, 19VCFP22
19VCYP22	14BE	19VATP22, 19VBRP22, 19VCTP22, 19VDTP22, 19VDXP22

Tube Type	Basing	Replacement
19VDAP4	8HR	
19VDCP22	14BP	19VFXP22
19VDEP4	8HR	19VCKP4
19VDFP22	14BE	19VBRP22, 19VCTP22, 19VDQP22, 19VEAP22, 19VEDP22, 19VEHP22
19VDGP4	8HR	19VBZP4
19VDHP4	8HR	19VARP4
19VDKP22	13D	
19VDMP22	14BE	19VAQP22, 19VCSP22, 19VDUP22, 19VEFP22, 19VEGP22, 19VEWP22
19VDNP22	14BE	19VAQP22
19VDQP22	14BE	19VBWP22[1], 19VEAP22, 19VEBP22
19VDRP22	13D	19VEMP22, 19VGMP22
19VDSP22	14BE	19VCFP22, 19VCTP22, 19VEDP22, 19VEHP22, 19VHJP22
19VDTP22	14BE	19VBRP22, 19VCTP22, 19VDFP22, 19VDQP22, 19VDSP22, 19VEDP22, 19VHJP22, 19VSP22
19VDUP22	14BE	19VCSP22, 19VDMP22, 19VEFP22, 19VEGP22, 19VEWP22
19VDWP22	14BE	19VATP22, 19VCFP22, 19VCTP22, 19VDFP22, 19VEAP22, 19VEDP22, 19VHBP22, 19VHJP22
19VDXP22	14BE	19VATP22, 19VBRP22, 19VCRP22, 19VDFP22, 19VDQP22, 19VSP22
19VDYP22	14BE	19VBRP22, 19VCFP22, 19VCNP22
19VDZP22	14BE	
19VEAP22	14BE	19VATP22, 19VBRP22, 19VBWP22[1], 19VCRP22[1], 19VCTP22, 19VDFP22, 19VEBP22
19VEBP22	14BE	19VBWP22[1], 19VDQP22, 19VEAP22
19VEDP22	14BE	19VEHP22, 19VEKP22, 19VHBP22, 19VHJP22
19VEFP22	14BE	19VCBP22, 19VCSP22, 19VDMP22, 19VDUP22, 19VEGP22
19VEGP22	14BE	19VEWP22
19VEHP22	14BE	19VETP22, 19VHBP22
19VEJP22	13D	
19VEKP22	14BE	19VGDP22, 19VELP22, 19VFAP22, 19VHBP22, 19VHJP22
19VELP22	14BE	19VEDP22, 19VEKP22, 19VHBP22, 19VHJP22
19VEMP4	8HR	19VBNP4, A
19VENP4	8HR	19VARP4, 19VDHP4, 19VERP4
19VEQP22	13D	19VDRP22, 19VGMP22
19VERP4	8HR	19VARP4, 19VDHP4, 19VENP4
19VETP22	14BE	19VEHP22, 19VHBP22
19VEUP22	14BE	19VEDP22, 19VEHP22, 19VEKP22, 19VHBP22, 19VHJP22
19VEWP22	14BE	19VEGP22
19VEXP22	14BE	
19VEZP22	14BE	19VEDP22, 19VEKP22, 19VELP22, 19VHBP22, 19VHJP22
19VFAP22	14BE	19VEDP22, 19VEKP22, 19VELP22, 19VHBP22, 19VHJP22
19VFBP22	14BP	19VFJP22
19VFDP4	8HR	
19VFEP4	8HR	

Tube Type	Basing	Replacement
19VFGP4	8HR	
19VFJP22	14BP	19VFBP22
19VFKP22	13L	
19VFQP22	14BE	
19VFTP4	8HR	
19VFWP4	8HR	
19VFXP22	14BP	19VDCP22
19VFYP4	8HR	
19VFZP4	8HR	
19VGAP4	8HR	
19VGCP4	8HR	19VGFP4[1]
19VGDP4	8HR	
19VGEP4	8HR	
19VGFP4	8HR	19VGCP4[1]
19VGKP22	13L	
19VGLP22	14BP	
19VGMP22	13D	
19VGQP22	13G	19VHFP22
19VGSP4	8HR	
19VGUP4	8HR	
19VGXP4	8HR	19VAHP4
19VGYP4	8HR	19VEHP4
19VGZP22	13K	
19VHBP22	14BE	19VEHP22, 19VEKP22, 19VETP22, 19VEUP22, 19VHJP22
19VHCP22	14BE	
19VHEP4	8HR	19VGYP4
19VHFP22	13G	19VGQP22
19VHGP4	8HR	19VAHP4, 19VGXP4
19VHJP22	14BE	19VEDP22, 19VEKP22, 19VEUP22, 19VHBP22
19VHKP22	13G	
19VHSP22	13K	
19VHTP22	13K	
19VHUP4	8HR	
19VHWP22	13B	
19VHXP22	14BP	
19VHYP22	13L	
19VJAP4	8HR	
19VJBP22	13M	19VJQP22
19VJDP22	13P	
19VJFP22	13N	
19VJGP4	8HR	
19VJMP22	13N	19VJTP22
19VJNP22	13K	
19VJQP22	13M	19VJBP22
19VJSP22	14BE	
19VJTP22	13N	19VJMP22
19VJUP22	13N	
19VJWP22	13L	
19VJYP22	13M	

Tube Type	Basing	Replacement
19VKDP22	13N	
19VKEP22	13N	
19VKNP22	14BE	
19VKRP22	14BE	19VKTP22
19VKSP22	13N	
19VKTP22	14BE	19VKRP22
19VKWP22	13B	
19VLAP22	14BE	
19VLBP22	13B	
19VP22	14W	
19VSP22	14BE	
19VUP4	8HR	
19XP4	8HR	19AVP4, 19AXP4[1], 19AYP4[1]
19YP4	8JR	19ANP4[1], 19AVP4
19ZP4	8JS	19AQP4[1], 19AVP4, 19BHP4
20ABP4	8HR	19VCJP4, 19VCLP4, 19VCMP4, 20RP4, 20YP4, 20ZP4
20ADP4	8HR	19VERP4
20AEP4	8HR	19VCMP4, 20SP4†
20AFP4	8HR	20AFP4A
20AFP4A	8HR	
20AGP4	8HR	
20AHP4	8HR	19VBUP4, 19VBNP4A, 19VEMP4
20AKP4	8HR	
20BP4	12D	
20CP4	12D	20CP4B, C, 20DP4, B, 20CP4A[7], D[7], 20DP4A[7], C[7], D*[7]
20CP4A	12N	20CP4D, 20DP4A, C, 20CP4[6], B[6], C[6], 20DP4[6], B[6], D*
20CP4B	12D	20CP4, C, 20DP4, B, 20CP4A[7], D[7], 20DP4A[7], C[7], D*[7]
20CP4C	12D	20CP4, B, 20DP4, B, 20CP4A[7], D[7], 20DP4A[7], C[7], D*[7]
20CP4D	12N	20CP4A, 20DP4A, C, 20CP4[6], B[6], C[6], 20DP4[6], B[6], D*
20DP4	12D	20DP4B, 20CP4, B, C, 20DP4A[7], C[7], D*[7], 20CP4A[7], D[7]
20DP4A	12N	20DP4C, 20CP4A, D, 20DP4[6], B[6], D*, 20CP4[6], B[6], C[6]
20DP4B	12D	20DP4, 20CP4, B, C, 20DP4A[7], C[7], D*[7], 20CP4A[7], D[7]
20DP4C	12N	20DP4A, 20CP4A, D,

Tube Type	Basing	Replacement
		20DP4[6], B[6], D*, 20CP4[6], B[6], C[6]
20DP4D	12N	20DP4A**, C**, 20CP4A**, D**
20FP4	12M	20GP4[7]
20GP4	12L	20FP4[6]
20HP4	12M	20HP4B, C, A[7], D[7], E*[7], 20JP4[7], 20LP4[7], 20MP4[7]
20HP4A	12L	20HP4D, 20JP4, 20LP4, 20MP4, 20HP4[6], B[6], C[6], E*
20HP4B	12M	20HP4, C, A[7], D[7], E*[7], 20JP4[7], 20LP4[7], 20MP4[7]
20HP4C	12M	20HP4, B, A[7], D[7], E*[7], 20JP4[7], 20LP4[7], 20MP4[7]
20HP4D	12L	20HP4A, 20JP4, 20LP4, 20MP4, 20HP4[6], B[6], C[6], E*
20HP4E	12L	20HP4A**, 20JP4**, 20LP4**, 20MP4**
20JP4	12P	
20LP4	12L	20HP4A, D, 20JP4, 20MP4, 20HP4[6], B[6], C[6], E*
20MP4	12L	20HP4A, D, 20JP4, 20LP4, 20HP4[6], B[6], C[6], E*
20RP4	8HR	19VCJP4, 19VCLP4, 19VCMP4, 19VEMP4, 20AB4, 20YP4, 20ZP4
20SP4	8HR	19VCJP4, 19VCLP4, 19VCMP4, 20AEP4†
20TP4	8HR	20XP4
20UP4	8HR	19VALP4
20VADP22	14BE	20VAGP22
20VAEP22	14BE	
20VAFP22	14BE	
20VAGP22	14BE	20VADP22
20VAHP22	14BH	22ALP22
20VAJP22	14BE	20VASP22, 22ALP22
20VAKP22	14BE	20VALP22
20VALP22	14BE	20VAKP22
20VAMP22	14BE	20VANP22
20VANP22	14BE	20VAMP22
20VASP22	14BE	20VAFP22
20VATP4	8HR	
20VAQP4	8HR	
20WP4	8HR	
20WP4A	8HR	20WP4

Tube Type	Basing	Replacement
20XP4	8HR	19VCKP4
20YP4	8HR	19VCLP4, 19VCMP4, 20ABP4, 20RP4, 20ZP4
20ZP4	8HR	19VCMP4, 20ABP4, 20RP4, 20YP4
21ACP4	12N	21ACP4A, 21AMP4, A, 21BSP4, 21CUP4, 21AMP4B*
21ACP4A	12N	21ACP4, 21AMP4, A, 21BSP4, 21CUP4, 21AMP4B*
21AFP4	12M	21BCP4*[7], 21YP4[7], A[7], B*[7]
21ALP4	12L	21ALP4A, B, 21ATP4, A, B, 21BTP4, 21CMP4, 21CWP4, 21DNP4
21ALP4A	12L	21ALP4, B, 21ATP4, 21ATP4A, 21ATP4B, 21BTP4, 21CMP4, 21CWP4, 21DNP4
21ALP4B	12L	21ALP4, A, 21ATP4, A, B, 21BTP4, 21CMP4, 21CWP4, 21DNP4
21AMP4	12N	21AMP4A, 21ACP4, A, 21BSP4, 21CUP4, 21AMP4B*
21AMP4A	12N	21AMP4, 21ACP4, A, 21BSP4, 21CUP4, 21AMP4B*
21AMP4B	12N	21AMP4**, A**, 21ACP4**, A**, 21BSP4**, 21CUP4**
21ANP4	12M	21ANP4A
21ANP4A	12M	21ANP4
21AP4	12D	
21AQP4	12D	21AQP4A, 21ACP4[7], A[7], 21AMP4[7], A[7], B*[7], 21BSP4[7], 21CUP4[7]
21AQP4A	12D	21AQP4, 21ACP4[7], A[7], 21AMP4[7], A[7], B*[7], 21BSP4[7], 21CUP4[7]
21ARP4	12N	21ARP4A
21ARP4A	12N	21ARP4
21ASP4	12M	21AYP4[7], 21XP4[7], 21XP4A[7], 21XP4B*[7]
21ATP4	12L	21ATP4A, B, 21ALP4,

Tube Type	Basing	Replacement	Tube Type	Basing	Replacement
		A, B, 21BTP4, 21CMP4, 21CWP4, 21DNP4, 21BAP4*, 21BNP4*, 21CVP4*			B, 21CVP4, 21DRP4, 21FLP4
21ATP4A	12L	21ATP4, B, 21ALP4B, 21BTP4, 21CMP4, 21CWP4, 21DNP4, 21BAP4*, 21BNP4*, 21CVP4*	21BCP4	12L	21YP4B, 21YP4**, 21YP4A**
21ATP4B	12L	21ATP4, A, 21ALP4, A, B, 21BTP4, 21CMP4, 21CWP4, 21DNP4, 21BAP4*, 21BNP4*, 21CVP4*	21BDP4	12L	21AUP4C, 21AVP4C, 21AUP4B**, 21AVP4B**
			21BNP4	12L	21BAP4, 21CBP4A, 21CVP4, 21DRP4, 21FLP4
21AUP4	12L	21AUP4A, B, C*, 21AVP4, 21AVP4A, 21AVP4B, 21AVP4C*, 21BDP4*	21BRP4	8GM	
			21BSP4	12N	21ACP4, A, 21AMP4, A, 21CUP4, 21AMP4B*
21AUP4A	12L	21AUP4, B, C*, 21AVP4, 21AVP4A, 21AVP4B, 21AVP4C*, 21BDP4*	21BTP4	12L	21ALP4B[1], 21ATP4A[1], 21BAP4[1], 21BNP4*[1], 21CMP4[1], 21CVP4*[1], 21CWP4[1], 21DNP4[1]
21AUP4B	12L	21AUP4, A, C*, 21AVP4, 21AVP4A, 21AVP4B, 21AVP4C*, 21BDP4*	21CBP4	12L	21CBP4A, B, 21DLP4, 21DQP4, 21DRP4, 21FLP4, 21CKP4[1]
21AUP4C	12L	21AVP4C, 21BDP4, 21AUP4**, A**, B**, 21AVP4**, A**, B**	21CBP4A	12L	21CBP4B, 21DLP4, 21DQP4, 21DRP4, 21FLP4, 21CKP4[1]
21AVP4	12L	21AVP4A, B, C*, 21AUP4, A, B, C*, 21BDP4*	21CBP4B	12L	12CBP4A, 21DLP4, 21DQP4, 21DRP4, 21FLP4, 21CKP4[1]
			21CDP4	12L	21CDP4A, 21CKP4*[1]
21AVP4A	12L	21AVP4, B, C*, 21AUP4, A, B, C*, 21BDP4*	21CDP4A	12L	21CDP4, 21CKP4*[1]
			21CEP4	8HR	21EMP4
21AVP4B	12L	21AVP4, A, C*, 21AUP4, A, B, C*, 21BDP4*	21CEP4A	8HR	21DWP4[1]
			21CGP4	12L	21CHP4*
			21CHP4	12L	21CGP4**
21AVP4C	12L	21AUP4C, 21BDP4, 21AVP4**, A**, B**, 21AUP4**, A**, B**	21CKP4	12L	21CBP4A[1], 21DLP4[1], 21DRP4[1], 21FLP4[1]
			21CLP4	12AJ	
21AWP4	12N	21AWP4A*	21CMP4	12L	21DNP4, 21CBP4A*, 21CKP4[1], 21DRP4*, 21FLP4*
21AWP4A	12N	21AWP4**			
21AXP22	14W		21CQP4	7FA	21CSP4[1]
21AXP22A	14W		21CSP4	7FA	21CQP4[1]
21AYP4	12L	21XP4, A, B*, 21ASP4[6]	21CUP4	12N	21ACP4, A, 21AMP4, 21AMP4A, 21BSP4, 21AMP4B*
21BAP4	12L	21BNP4, 21CBP4A,	21CVP4	12L	21BAP4, 21BNP4, 21CMP4, 21DNP4
			21CWP4	12L	21ALP4B, 21ATP4A, 21BTP4, 21CMP4, 21DNP4
			21CXP4	12L	21DSP4[1]

Tube Type	Basing	Replacement
21CYP22	*14AL*	
21CYP22A	*14AL*	
21CZP4	*8HR*	21DEP4*, A*, 21DHP4[1]*, 21DKP4[1]*, A[1]*
21DAP4	*8HR*	21DMP4[1]
21DEP4	*8HR*	21DEP4A, 21CZP4**, 21DHP4[1], 21DKP4[1], 21DKP4A[1]
21DEP4A	*8HR*	21DEP4
21DFP4	*8HR*	21CZP4*[1], 21DEP4[1], A[1], 21DWP4, 21EMP4
21DHP4	*8HR*	21CEP4, A, 21DMP4, 21DKP4[1], A[1]
21DJP4	*12L*	21CBP4A[1], 21CKP4[1], 21DLP4[1], 21DRP4[1], 21FLP4[1]
21DKP4	*8HR*	21DKP4A, 21DEP4[1], A[1], 21DHP4[1]
21DKP4A	*8HR*	21DKP4, 21DEP4[1], A[1], 21DHP4[1]
21DLP4	*12L*	21DQP4
21DMP4	*8HR*	
21DNP4	*12L*	21CBP4A*[1], 21CKP4*[1], 21CMP4[1], 21DRP4*[1], 21FLP4*[1]
21DP4	*12M*	
21DQP4	*12L*	21CBP4[1], A[1], B[1], 21CKP4[1], 21DLP4[1], 21FLP4[1]
21DRP4	*12L*	21CBP4A, 21DLP4, 21FLP4, 21CKP4[1]
21DSP4	*12L*	21CXP4
21DVP4	*12L*	21ENP4, 21CKP4*[1], 21DJP4*[1]
21DWP4	*8HR*	21CEP4A[1], 21DFP4[1]
21EAP4	*8JK*	
21ELP4	*12L*	
21EMP4	*8HR*	
21ENP4	*12L*	21CBP4A*[1], 21CKP4*[1], 21CMP4[1], 21DJP4*[1], 21DNP4[1], 21DRP4*[1], 21FLP4*[1]
21EP4	*12D*	21EP4A[7], B[7], C[7]*, 21ZP4C
21EP4A	*12N*	21EP4B, C*, 21ZP4C
21EP4B	*12N*	21EP4A, C*, 21ZP4C

Tube Type	Basing	Replacement
21EP4C	*12N*	21EP4A**, B**, 21ZP4C
21EQP4	*8JR*	
21ERP4	*8JR*	
21ESP4	*8JS*	21FAP4
21EVP4	*8JK*	
21EXP4	*8JR*	21EQP4[1]
21EZP4	*8JR*	
21FAP4	*8JR*	
21FBP22	*14AU*	
21FBP22A	*14AU*	21GUP22
21FCP4	*8HR*	
21FDP4	*8KW*	
21FJP22	*14AU*	21FKP22
21FJP22A	*14AU*	
21FKP22	*14AU*	21FJP22
21FLP4	*12L*	21CBP4A, 21DLP4, 21DRP4, 21CKP4[1]
21FMP4	*8HR*	
21FP4	*12M*	21FP4A[7], D*[7]
21FP4A	*12L*	21FP4[6], D*
21FP4C	*12L*	21FP4[6], 21FP4A, D*
21FP4D	*12L*	21FP4A**, C**
21FUP4	*8HR*	21GTP4[1]
21FVP4	*8HR*	21FWP4
21FWP4	*8HR*	21FVP4
21FXP4	*8HR*	
21FYP4	*8HR*	
21FZP4	*8HR*	
21GAP4	*8HR*	21GAP4A
21GAP4A	*8HR*	21GAP4
21GBP4	*8HR*	
21GCP4	*8HR*	
21GEP4	*8HR*	
21GFP22	*14BE*	20VAGP22
21GHP4	*8HR*	
21GJP4	*8HR*	
21GKP4	*8HR*	
21GSP4	*8HR*	
21GTP4	*8HR*	21FUP4[1]
21GUP22	*14AU*	21FBP22
21GVP22	*14AU*	21GYP22
21GWP22	*14BE*	20VAGP22, 21HBP22
21GYP22	*14AU*	21GVP22
21HBP22	*14BE*	21GWP22
21JP4	*12N*	21JP4A
21JP4A	*12N*	21JP4
21KP4	*12D*	21KP4A[7]
21KP4A	*12P*	21FP4D, 21KP4[6]
21MP4	*12M*	
21VABP22	*14BE*	21VAKP22, 22AMP22
21VACP22	*14BE*	21VAJP22, 21VAKP22,

Tube Type	Basing	Replacement	Tube Type	Basing	Replacement
		21VAQP22, 21VAUP22, 21VAZP22, 21VBEP22	22AP4	12D	22AP4A
			22AP4A	12D	22AP4
			22AQP22	14BE	
			22ARP22	14BE	20VAGP22
			22ASP22	14BE	22UP22
21VADP22	14BE	21VARP22, 21VBEP22	22ATP22	14BE	
21VAGP4	8HR		22JP22	14BE	20VAGP22, 22ARP22
21VAKP22	14BE		22KP22	14BE	
21VALP22	14BE	21VAXP22, 21VBCP22	22QP22	14BE	20VAGP22, 22ARP22, 22JP22
21VAQP22	14BE	21VAUP22, 21VAZP22, 21VBEP22, 21VBHP22	22RP22	14BE	22KP22, 22UP22
			22SP22	14BE	20VAGP22, 20VAMP22, 20VANP22
21VARP22	14BE	21VBEP22			
21VASP4	8HR	22ZP4			
21VATP4	8HR	22AFP4	22TP4	8HR	
21VAUP22	14BE	21VAKP22, 21VAQP22, 21VAZP22, 21VBEP22, 21VBHP22	22UP22	14BE	22ASP22
			22VABP4	8HR	22VAHP4[1]
			22VACP4	8HR	
			22VADP4	12L	
			22VAEP4	8HR	
21VAXP22	14BE	21VBCP22	22VAGP4	8HR	
21VAZP22	14BE	21VAQP22, 21VAUP22, 21VBEP22, 21VBHP22	22VAHP4	8HR	
			22VAMP4	8HR	22VANP4, A, 23GBP4, 23HFP4
			22VANP4	8HR	22VAMP4
21VBCP22	14BE	21VAXP22	22VANP4A	8HR	22VAMP4
21VBEP22	14BE	21VBHP22	22VARP4	8HR	23GJP4, 23GWP4
21VBHP22	14BE	21VBEP22	22VASP4	8HR	23FCP4, 23FDP4, 23FHP4
21VBJP22	14BE				
21VBLP22	14BP		22VATP4	8HR	23HGP4, 23JEP4
21WP4	12N	21WP4A, B*	22VAUP4	8HR	
21WP4A	12N	21WP4, B*	22VAXP4	8HR	22VABP4, 22VAZP4, 22VBDP4
21WP4B	12N	21WP4**, A**	22VAYP4	8HR	23JQP4
21XP4	12L	21XP4A, B*	22VAZP4	8HR	22VABP4, 22VAXP4, 22VBDP4
21XP4A	12L	21XP4, B*			
21XP4B	12L	21XP4**, A**	22VBAP4	8HR	22VAXP4, 22VAZP4, 22VBDP4
21YP4	12L	21YP4A, B*, 21BCP4*			
21YP4A	12L	21YP4, B*, 21BCP4*	22VBCP4	8HR	
21YP4B	12L	21BCP4, 21YP4**, A**	22VBDP4	8HR	22VAXP4, 22VAZP4
			22WP22	14BE	
21ZP4	12D	21ZP4A[7], 21ZP4B[7], 21ZP4C*[7]	22YP22	14BE	
21ZP4A	12N	21ZP4B, C*	22ZP4	8HR	21VASP4
21ZP4B	12N	21ZP4A, C*	23ACP4	12L	23TP4
21ZP4C	12N	21ZP4A**, B**	23AFP4	12L	23BMP4, 23BTP4, 23YP4, 23CDP4[1]
22ADP22	14BE				
22AEP22	14BE		23AHP4	12L	23ASP4, 23AUP4, 23CZP4, 23AZP4[1]
22AFP4	12D	21VATP4			
22AHP22	14BE	20VAKP22, 20VALP22, 22ASP22, 22UP22	23AKP4	8JR	23CVP4[1]
			23ALP4	8HR	23AMP4[1], 23CQP4[1], 23MP4[1], 23MP4A[1], 23VP4[1]
22ALP22	14BE	20VAJP22, 20VASP22			
22AMP22	14BE	21VABP22, 21VAKP22	23AMP4	8HR	23ALP4[1], 23CQP4[1],
22ANP22	14BH	20VAHP22			

Tube Type	Basing	Replacement
		23MP4[1], 23MP4A[1], 23VP4[1]
23ANP4	12L	23ATP4, 23BKP4, 23BLP4
23AQP4	8HR	23AMP4, 23VP4, 23ALP4[1], 23AMP4[1], 23CQP4[1], 23FP4[1], A[1], 23MP4[1], 23MP4A[1]
23ARP4	8HR	23AXP4[1]
23ASP4	12L	
23ATP4	12L	23ANP4, 23BKP4, 23BLP4
23AUP4	12L	23AHP4, 23ASP4, 23CZP4, 23AZP4[1]
23AVP4	8HR	23CP4, A, 23DXP4, 23AYP4[1], 23BSP4[1], 23HP4[1], 23SP4[1]
23AWP4	12L	23BJP4
23AXP4	8HR	23EJP4
23AYP4	8HR	23BSP4, 23SP4, 23AVP4[1], 23CP4[1], A[1], 23DXP4[1], 23HP4[1]
23AZP4	12L	23ASP4[1]
23BAP4	8HR	23BP4
23BCP4	8HR	23CEP4[1], 23CMP4[1]
23BDP4	12L	23BTP4
23BEP4	8HR	23BEP4A
23BEP4A	8HR	23BEP4
23BGP4	8HR	23BHP4
23BHP4	8HR	23BGP4
23BJP4	12L	23AWP4
23BKP4	12L	23BLP4, 23ANP4[1], 23ATP4[1]
23BLP4	12L	23BKP4, 23ANP4[1], 23ATP4[1]
23BMP4	12L	23AFP4, 23BTP4, 23XP4, 23YP4, 23CDP4[1]
23BNP4	8HR	23ADP4, 23AVP4, 23CP4, A, 23DXP4, 23GP4, 23AYP4[1], 23BEP4[1], A[1], 23BQP4[1], 23BSP4[1], 23CBP4[1], 23SP4[1], 23UP4[1]
23BP4	8HR	23BAP4, 23CP4A
23BQP4	8HR	23CBP4, 23UP4, 23DGP4[1]
23BRP4	8JR	23BYP4, 23CSP4, 23RP4, 23CUP4[1], 23DP4[1]
23BSP4	8HR	23AVP4[1], 23AYP4[1],
		23CP4[1], A[1], 23DXP4[1], 23GP4[1], 23HP4[1], 23SP4[1]
23BTP4	12L	23AFP4, 23BMP4, 23XP4, 23YP4, 23CDP4[1]
23BVP4	12L	23CTP4[1], 23EAP4[1]
23BXP4	12L	23EDP4
23BYP4	8JR	23BRP4, 23CSP4, 23RP4, 23CUP4[1], 23DP4[1]
23BZP4	12L	
23CAP4	12L	
23CBP4	8HR	23BQP4, 23UP4
23CDP4	12L	
23CEP4	8HR	23ARP4[1], 23CMP4[1]
23CGP4	12L	23ASP4[1]
23CMP4	8HR	23BCP4[1]
23CP4	8HR	23CP4A, 23AVP4, 23DXP4, 23AYP4[1], 23BSP4[1], 23HP4[1], 23SP4[1]
23CP4A	8HR	23CP4, 23AVP4, 23DXP4, 23AYP4[1], 23BSP4[1], 23HP4[1], 23SP4[1]
23CQP4	8HR	23FP4[1], A[1], 23VP4[1]
23CSP4	8JR	23BRP4, 23BYP4, 23RP4, 23CUP4[1], 23DP4[1]
23CTP4	12L	23BVP4[1], 23EAP4[1]
23CUP4	8JR	23DP4, 23BRP4[1], 23BYP4[1], 23CSP4[1], 23RP4[1]
23CVP4	8JR	23AKP4[1]
23CWP4	8JR	23CXP4[1]
23CXP4	8JR	23CWP4[1]
23CZP4	12L	23ASP4
23DAP4	8HR	23DCP4[1]
23DBP4	8HR	23NP4
23DCP4	8HR	23DAP4[1]
23DEP4	8HR	
23DFP4	8HR	
23DHP4	8HR	23DJP4, 23UP4[1]
23DJP4	8HR	23DHP4, 23UP4[1]
23DKP4	12L	23DTP4, 23FLP4[1]
23DLP4	12L	23DLP4A, 23ENP4, 23FBP4, 23FWP4[1], 23FWP4A[1]
23DLP4A	12L	23DLP4, 23ENP4, 23FBP4, 23FWP4[1], A[1]
23DNP4	12L	
23DP4	8JR	23CUP4, 23RBP4[1],

Tube Type	Basing	Replacement
		23BYP4¹, 23CSP4¹, 23RP4¹
23DQP4	8HR	
23DSP4	8HR	23DSP4A
23DSP4A	8HR	23DSP4
23DTP4	12L	23DKP4, 23FLP4¹
23DVP4	8HR	23DVP4A, 23DZP4¹, 23EWP4¹, A¹
23DVP4A	8HR	23DVP4, 23DZP4¹, 23EWP4¹, A¹
23DWP4	8HR	23GHP4¹
23DYP4	8HR	22VANP4, A, 23ESP4¹, 23FVP4¹
23DZP4	8HR	23EWP4, A, 23DVP4¹, A¹
23EAP4	12L	23BVP4¹, 23CTP4¹
23ECP4	12L	
23EDP4	12L	
23EFP4	8HR	23FCP4¹, 23FDP4¹, 23FHP4¹, 23GJP4¹, A¹, 23GWP4¹
23EGP22	14BE	
23EKP4	12L	23FLP4
23ELP4	12L	
23ENP4	12L	23DLP4, A, 23FBP4, 23FWP4¹, A¹
23EP4	8KP	
23EQP4	8HR	23ERP4¹, 23EWP4A
23ERP4	8HR	23EQP4¹
23ESP4	8HR	22VANP4, A, 23DYP4¹, 23ETP4¹, 23FVP4, A, 23GTP4
23ETP4	8HR	22VANP4¹, A¹, 23FVP4B¹, 23GTP4, 23FMP4¹, 23HMP4¹, 23HXP4¹
23EWP4	8HR	23EWP4A, 23DZP4, 23DVP4¹, A¹
23EWP4A	8HR	23EWP4, 23DZP4, 23DVP4¹, A¹
23EYP4	12L	
23EZP4	8HR	
23FAP4	8HR	23HLP4
23FBP4	12L	23DLP4, A, 23ENP4, 23FWP4¹, A¹
23FCP4	8HR	22VASP4, 23FDP4, 23FHP4, 23GJP4, A, 23GWP4, 23EFP4¹
23FDP4	8HR	22VASP4, 23FCP4, 23FHP4, 23GJP4, A, 23GWP4, 23EFP4¹
23FEP4	12L	
23FHP4	8HR	22VASP4, 23FCP4, 23FDP4, 23GJP4, A, 23GWP4, 23EFP4¹
23FKP4	8HR	
23FLP4	12L	23DKP4¹, 23GTP4¹
23FMP4	8HR	22VANP4, A, 23ETP4¹, 23FVP4B, 23GTP4¹, 23HMP4¹, 23HXP4
23FNP4	12L	
23FP4	8HR	23FP4A, 23VP4¹
23FP4A	8HR	23FP4, 23VP4¹
23FRP4	8HR	22VAHP4¹, 23JFP4¹
23FSP4	8HR	23JBP4
23FVP4	8HR	22VANP4, A, 23FVP4A, 23DYP4¹, 23ESP4, 23ETP4¹, 23FMP4, 23HMP4
23FVP4A	8HR	22VANP4, A, 23FVP4, 23DYP4¹, 23ESP4, 23ETP4¹, 23FMP4, 23HMP4
23FVP4B	8HR	22VAMP4
23FWP4	12L	23FWP4A, 23DLP4¹, A¹, 23ENP4¹, 23FBP4¹
23FWP4A	12L	23FWP4, 23DLP4¹, A¹, 23ENP4¹, 23FBP4¹
23GBP4	8HR	22VAMP4, 23HFP4, A
23GDP4	8HR	23DVP4, A, 23DZP4¹, 23EWP4¹, A¹
23GFP4	8HR	
23GHP4	8HR	23DWP4¹
23GJP4	8HR	22VAHP4¹, 22VARP4, 23GJP4A, 23GWP4
23GJP4A	8HR	22VAHP4¹, 22VARP4, 23GJP4, 23GWP4
23GKP4	12L	23GRP4¹
23GP4	8HR	23AVP4, 23CP4, A, 23HP4, 23ADP4¹, 23AYP4¹, 23BSP4¹, 23SP4¹
23GRP4	12L	23GKP4¹
23GSP4	8HR	23HZP4¹
23GTP4	8HR	23ETP4, 23FMP4¹, 23HMP4¹, 23HXP4¹
23GUP4	8HR	
23GVP4	8HR	22VABP4
23GWP4	8HR	22VAHP4, 22VARP4, 23GJP4, A

Tube Type	Basing	Replacement
23GXP4	8HR	23HQP4[1]
23GYP4	12L	
23HAP4	12L	
23HBP4	8HR	
23HCP4	8HR	
23HFP4	8HR	22VAMP4, 23HFP4A, 23GBP4
23HFP4A	8HR	22VAMP4, 23HFP4, 23GBP4
23HGP4	8HR	22VATP4, 23JEP4
23HKP4	8HR	
23HLP4	8HR	
23HMP4	8HR	23DYP4[1], 23ESP4[1], 23ETP4[1], 23FMP4[1], 23FVP4[1], A[1], 23GTP4[1], 23HXP4[1]
23HP4	8HR	22VANP4[1], A[1], 23AVP4, 23CP4, A, 23DXP4, 23AYP4[1], 23BSP4[1], 23FVP4B[1], 23SP4[1]
23HQP4	8HR	23GXP4[1]
23HQP4A	8HR	23GXP4[1]
23HRP4	8HR	23HWP4
23HTP4	8HR	
23HUP4	8HR	23HUP4A, 23JLP4
23HUP4A	8HR	23HUP4, 23JLP4
23HWP4	8HR	23HWP4A
23HWP4A	8HR	23HWP4
23HXP4	8HR	23ETP4[1], 23FMP4, 23GTP4[1], 23HMP4[1]
23HZP4	8HR	23GSP4[1], 23HGP4[1]
23JBP4	8HR	
23JEP4	8HR	22VATP4, 23HGP4, 23HZP4[1]
23JEP4A	8HR	22VATP4, 23HGP4, 23HZP4[1]
23JFP4	8HR	22VAHP4[1], 23FRP4[1]
23JGP4	8HR	23FRP4
23JHP4	8HR	
23JLP4	8HR	22VAHP4[1], 23HUP4, A
23JP4	7FA	
23JQP4	8HR	22VAYP4
23JRP4	8HR	23FP4A
23KP4	8JS	23KP4A
23KP4A	8JS	23KP4
23MP4	8HR	23MP4A, 23ALP4[1], 23AMP4[1], 23CQP4[1], 23VP4[1]
23MP4A	8HR	23MP4, 23ALP4[1], 23AMP4[1], 23CQP4[1], 23VP4[1]
23NP4	8HR	

Tube Type	Basing	Replacement
23RP4	8JR	22VAHP4[1], 23BRP4, 23BYP4, 23CSP4, 23CUP4[1], 23DP4[1]
23SP4	8HR	23AYP4, 23BSP4, 23AVP4[1], 23CP4[1], A[1], 23DXP4[1], 23UP4[1]
23TP4	12L	23ACP4, 23BTP4
23UP4	8HR	23BQP4, 23CBP4
23VABP22	14BE	23VALP22, 23VANP22, 23VAXP22, 23VBSP22
23VACP22	14BE	23VADP22, 23VALP22, 23VANP22, 23VAQP22, 23VARP22, 23VBRP22, 23VBTP22
23VADP22	14BE	23VACP22, 23VAMP22, 23VAYP22, 23VBYP22, 23VCFP22
23VAEP22	14BE	23VAJP22
23VAHP22	14BE	23VATP22, 23VBRP22, 23VBYP22
23VAJP22	14BE	23VAEP22
23VALP22	14BE	23VAHP22, 23VANP22, 23VARP22
23VAMP22	14BE	23VADP22, 23VAQP22, 23VBWP22, 23VBYP22, 23VCFP22
23VANP22	14BE	23VAHP22, 23VALP22, 23VARP22, 23VATP22
23VAQP22	14BE	23VAMP22, 23VDBP22, 23VBRP22, 23VBWP22, 23VCFP22
23VARP22	14BE	23VAHP22, 23VALP22, 23VANP22
23VASP22	14BE	
23VATP22	14BE	23VAHP22, 23VALP22, 23VANP22

Tube Type	Basing	Replacement
23VAXP22	14BE	23VABP22, 23VALP22, 23VANP22, 23VATP22, 23VBSP22
23VAYP22		23VACP22, 23VADP22, 23VAQP22, 23VBAP22, 23VCFP22
23VAZP22	14BE	23VATP22
23VBAP22	14BE	23VACP22, 23VALP22, 23VAMP22, 23VAQP22, 23VBWP22, 23VBYP22, 23VCFP22
23VBCP22	14BE	23VAQP22, 23VBDP22
23VBDP22	14BE	23VAQP22, 23VBAP22, 23VBWP22, 23VBYP22, 23VCFP22
23VBFP22	14BE	23VBUP22
23VBGP22	14BE	
23VBHP22	14BE	25SP22
23VBJP22	14BE	
23VBKP22	14BE	23VBMP22
23VBMP22	14BE	
23VBNP22	14BE	23VAQP22, 23VAYP22, 23VBCP22, 23VBKP22, 25BKP22
23VBRP22	14BE	23VAHP22, 23VAMP22, 23VAQP22, 23BCFP22
23VBSP22	14BE	23VABP22, 23VALP22, 23VAXP22
23VBTP22	14BE	23VACP22, 23VANP22, 23VAQP22
23VBUP22	14BE	
23VBWP22	14BE	23VALP22, 23VAMP22, 23VAQP22, 23VBAP22, 23VCEP22
23VBYP22	14BE	23VADP22, 23VAHP22, 23VAMP22, 23VBAP22, 23VBDP22, 23VCFP22
23VCEP22	14BE	
23VCFP22	14BE	
23VCMP22	14BE	
23VP4	8HR	23ALP4[1], 23AMP4[1], 23CQP4[1], 23MP4[1], A[1]
23WP4	8HR	23FP4A
23XP4	12L	23AFP4, 23BMP4, 23BTP4, 23YP4, 23CDP4[1]
23YP4	12L	23AFP4, 23BMP4, 23BTP4, 23XP4, 23CDP4[1]
23ZP4	12L	23BKP4
24ADP4	12N	24CP4[1], A[1], B*[1], 24TP4[1], 24VP4[1], A[1]
24AEP4	12L	
24AHP4	8HR	24ALP4, 24AQP4[1], 24AWP4[1], 24AXP4[1]
24AJP4	12L	24ATP4
24ALP4	8HR	24AHP4, 24AQP4[1], 24AWP4[1], 24AXP4[1]
24AMP4	7FA	
24ANP4	12L	24DP4, A, 24AEP4*, 24ASP4*[1], 24AUP4*, 24YP4[1], 24ZP4*[1]
24AP4	12D	24AP4A
24AP4A	12D	24AP4
24AP4B	12D	24AP4
24AQP4	8HR	24AHP4[1], 24ALP4[1], 24AWP4[1], 24AXP4[1]
24ASP4	12L	24AEP4[1], 24AUP4[1]
24ATP4	12L	24AJP4[1]
24AUP4	12L	24AEP4
24AVP4	8JK	
24AWP4	8HR	
24AXP4	8HR	24AHP4[1], 24ALP4[1], 24AQP4[1], 24AWP4[1]
24BAP4	8HR	
24BCP4	12L	
24BEP4	8KW	
24BP4	12M	
24CP4	12N	24CP4A, 24ADP4, 24QP4, 24TP4, 24VP4, A, 24CP4B*

Tube Type	Basing	Replacement
24CP4A	12N	24CP4, 24ADP4, 24QP4, 24TP4, 24VP4, A, 24CP4B*
24CP4B	12N	24CP4**, A**, 24DP4**, 24QP4**, 24TP4**, 24VP4**, A**
24DP4	12L	24DP4A, 24ANP4, 24AEP4*, 24ASP4*[1], 24AUP4*, 24YP4[1], 24ZP4*[1]
24DP4A	12L	24DP4, 24ANP4, 24AEP4*, 24ASP4*[1], 24AUP4*, 24YP4[1], 24ZP4*[1]
24QP4	12N	24ADP4, 24CP4, A, 24TP4, 24VP4, 24VP4A, 24CP4B*
24TP4	12N	24ADP4, 24CP4, 24CP4A, 24QP4, 24VP4, 24VP4A, 24CP4B*
24VABP22	14BQ	A66-501X
24VP4	12N	24VP4A, 24ADP4, 24CP4, A, 24QP4, 24TP4, 24CP4B*
24VP4A	12N	24VP4, 24ADP4, 24CP4, 24CP4A, 24QP4, 24TP4, 24CP4B*
24XP4	12D	
24YP4	12L	24ANP4, 24AUP4, 24DP4, A, 24ZP4, 24TP4, 24AEP4*, 24ASP4[1]
24ZP4	12L	24AEP4, 24ANP4, 24AUP4, 24DP4, 24DP4A, 24YP4, 24ASP4[1]
25ABP22	14BE	23VALP22, 23VANP22, 23VARP22, 23VATP22, 25XP22
25ADP22	14BE	
25AEP22	14BE	23VANP22, 23VATP22 25YP22
25AFP22	14BE	23VALP22, 23VANP22, 23VARP22, 23VATP22, 25BMP22
25AJP22	14BE	23VADP22,

Tube Type	Basing	Replacement
		23VALP22, 23VANP22, 23VAQP22, 23VARP22, 23VBJP22, 23VBRP22, 23VBYP22, 25BHP22
25AKP22	14BE	
25ALP22	14BE	23VBMP22, 25ALP22A
25ALP22A	14BE	23VBMP22, 25ALP22
25AMP22	14BE	23VAEP22, 23VAJP22
25ANP22	14BE	23VABP22, 23VALP22, 23VANP22, 23VARP22, 25BAP22
25AP22	14BE	23VALP22, 23VANP22, 23VARP22, 25ABP22, 25XP22
25AP22A	14BE	23VALP22, 23VANP22, 23VARP22, 25ABP22, 25XP22
25AQP22	14BE	23VABP22, 23VAXP22
25ASP22	14BE	
25ATP22	14BE	
25AWP22	14BE	23VACP22, 23VALP22, 23VANP22, 23VAQP22, 23VARP22, 23VBNP22, 23VBTP22, 25BKP22
25AYP22	14BE	25ALP22, 25CAP22
25AZP22	14BE	23VACP22, 23VALP22, 23VANP22, 23VAQP22, 23VARP22, 23VBPR22, 23VBTP22
25BAP22	14BE	23VABP22, 23VALP22, 23VAXP22, 25ANP22, 25GP22A
25BCP22	14BE	23VALP22, 23VANP22
25BDP22	14BE	23VAQP22, 23VBAP22, 23VBYP22

Tube Type	Basing	Replacement
25BFP22	14BE	23VACP22, 23VALP22, 23VANP22, 23VAQP22, 23VARP22, 23VBTP22
25BGP22	14BE	23VALP22, 23VANP22, 23VARP22
25BHP22	14BE	23VALP22, 23VANP22, 23VAQP22, 23VARP22, 23VBRP22, 23VBYP22
25BKP22	14BE	23VAQP22, 23VBAP22
25BLP22	14BE	
25BMP22	14BE	23VALP22, 23VANP22, 23VARP22
25BP22	14BE	23VANP22, 23VATP22, 25YP22
25BP22A	14BE	23VANP22, 23VATP22, 25YP22
25CAP22	14BE	25ALP22, 25AYP22
25CBP22	14BE	
25CP22	14BE	23VALP22, 23VARP22, 25ABP22, 25AP22, 25XP22
25DP4	8HR	
25FP22	14BE	23VANP22, 25FP22A
25FP22A	14BE	23VANP22, 25FP22
25GP22A	14BE	23VABP22, 23VALP22, 23VANP22, 23VARP22, 25ABP22, 25ANP22, 25BAP22, 25GP22
25HP4	8HR	
25JP4	8HR	
25KP4	8HR	25LP4[1]
25LP4	8HR	25KP4[1]
25SP22	14BE	23VBHP22
25TP4	8HR	
25VABP22	14BE	25VADP22, 25VAJP22, 25VALP22[1], 25VAMP22, 25VATP22, 25VBMP22, 25VBXP22, 25VCGP22,

Tube Type	Basing	Replacement
		25VDAP22, 25VDEP22, 25VDJP22, 25VDXP22
25VACP22	14BE	25VAFP22, 25VAQP22, 25VBQP22, 25VBWP22, 25VBZP22, 25VCBP22, 25VCEP22, 25VCKP22, 25VCUP22, 25VCWP22, 25VCZP22, 25VDAP22, 25VDRP22, 25VDSP22, 25VDXP22, 25VEHP22, 25VEXP22
25VADP22	14BE	25VABP22, 25VALP22[1], 25VATP22, 25VBMP22, 25VBXP22, 25VCGP22, 25VCKP22, 25VDAP22, 25VDEP22, 25VDJP22,
25VAEP22	14BE	25VABP22, 25VADP22, 25VALP22[1], 25VBXP22, 25VCGP22, 25VCKP22, 25VDAP22, 25VDEP22, 25VDJP22, 25VDXP22
25VAFP22	14BE	25VABP22, 25VACP22, 25VAEP22, 25VAWP2, 25VBUP22, 25VBWP22, 25VCBP22, 25VCEP22, 25VCKP22, 25VCUP22, 25VCZP22, 25VDAP22,

Tube Type	Basing	Replacement	Tube Type	Basing	Replacement
		25VDRP22, 25VDXP22, 25VEHP22, 25VEXP22			25VDAP22, 25VDEP22, 25VDJP22, 25VDXP22
25VAGP22	14BE	25VBEP22, 25VBYP22, 25VCBP22, 25VCXP22, 25VDFP22, 26HP22	25VAUP22	14BE	25VBAP22
			25VAWP22	14BE	25VACP22, 25VAFP22, 25VAQP22, 25VBQP22, 25VBZP22, 25VCBP22, 25VCUP22, 25VCWP22, 25VDSP22, 25VEDP22, 25VEHP22
25VAJP22	14BE	25VABP22, 25VALP22, 25VCGP22, 25VCKP22			
25VAKP22	14BE	25VALP22, 25VBLP22, 25VCGP22, 25VCKP22[1]			
25VALP22	14BE	25VABP22[1], 25VADP22[1], 25VBMP22[1], 25VCGP22[1], 25VCKP22[1]	25VAXP22	14BE	25VBCP22, 25VCSP22, 25VDGP22, 25VDHP22, 26EP22
25VAMP22	14BE	25VABP22, 25VALP22[1], 25VATP22, 25VBXP22, 25VCKP22, 25VDAP22, 25VDEP22, 25VDJP22, 25VDXP22	25VAZP22	14BE	25VBGP22, 25VBRP22, 25VCBP22[1], 25VCHP22[1], 25VCRP22[1]
			25VBAP22	14BE	25VAUP22
			25VBCP22	14BE	25VAXP22, 25VCSP22, 25VDGP22, 25VDHP22
25VAQP22	14BE	25VABP22, 25VACP22, 25VAEP22, 25VAWP22, 25VBUP22, 25VCBP22, 25VCEP22, 25VCKP22, 25VCUP22, 25VCZP22, 25VDAP22, 25VDRP22, 25VEDP22, 25VEHP22, 25VEXP22	25VBDP22	14BE	
			25VBEP22	14BE	25VAGP22, 25VBTP22, 25VBYP22, 25VCDP22, 25VCTP22, 25VCXP22, 25VDFP22
			25VBGP22	14BE	25VAZP22, 25VBRP22, 25VCBP22[1], 25VCFP22, 25VCHP22[1], 25VCRP22[1], 25VCWP22[1]
25VARP22	14BE	25VASP22	25VBJP22	14BE	25VAXP22, 25VBEP22, 25VDHP22
25VASP22	14BE	25VARP22			
25VATP22	14BE	25VADP22, 25VAJP22, 25VAMP22, 25VBXP22, 25VCGP22, 25VCKP22,	25VBKP22	14BE	25VAGP22, 25VBEP22, 25VBYP22[1], 25VCDP22, 25VCTP22[1], 25VCXP22, 26HP22

Tube Type	Basing	Replacement	Tube Type	Basing	Replacement
25VBLP22	14BE	25VAEP22, 25VAKP22, 25VALP22, 25VCKP22[1], 25VEXP22			25VCNP22, 25VCUP22, 25VCWP22, 25VDCP22, 25VDRP22,
25VBMP22	14BE	25VABP22, 25VADP22, 25VALP22[1], 25VCKP22, 25VDAP22, 25VDEP22, 25VDXP22			25VEBP22, 25VEDP22, 25VEHP22, 25VEXP22, 26DP22
25VBNP22	14BE	25VCNP22, 25VEBP22	25VCBP22	14BE	25VAWP22, 25VAZP22[1], 25VBGP22, 25VBNP22, 25VBRP22, 25VBWP22, 25VCEP22, 25VCFP22, 25VCRP22, 25VCUP22, 25VCYP22, 25VEXP22
25VBQP22	14BE	25VAWP22, 25VBWP22, 25VCFP22, 25VCNP22, 25VCUP22, 25VCZP22, 25VEBP22, 25VEDP22			
25VBRP22	14BE	25VCBP22[1], 25VCFP22[1], 25VCHP22[1], 25VCRP22[1], 25VCYP22[1]	25VCDP22	14BE	25BYP22, 25CMP22, 25VCTP22
25VBSP22	14BE		25VCEP22	14BE	25VAFP22, 25VAQP22, 25VBQP22, 25VBZP22, 25VCBP22, 25VCUP22, 25VCWP22, 25VCZP22, 25VDRP22, 25VDSP22, 25VEDP22, 25VEHP22, 25VEXP22
25VBTP22	14BE	25VBYP22, 25VCDP22, 25VDFP22			
25VBUP22	14BE	25VEXP22			
25VBWP22	14BE	25VACP22, 25VAFP22, 25VAQP22, 25VBQP22, 25VBZP22, 25VCBP22, 25VCEP22, 25VCUP22, 25VCWP22, 25VCZP22, 25VDRP22, 25VEAP22, 25VEDP22, 25VEXP22	25VCFP22	14BE	25VBNP22, 25VCBP22, 25VCRP22, 25VCUP22, 25VCYP22, 25VEBP22
			25VCGP22	14BE	25VALP22[1], 25VCKP22
25VBXP22	14BE	25VATP22, 25VDJP22	25VCHP22	14BE	25VAZP22[1], 25VBGP22[1], 25VBNP22, 25VBRP22[1], 25VCBP22, 25VCRP22, 25VCYP22, 25EBP22
25VBYP22	14BE	25VCDP22, 25VCMP22, 25VCTP22			
25VBZP22	14BE	25VAWP22, 25VBQP22, 25VBWP22, 285VCBP22, 25VCEP22,	25VCJP22	14BE	
			25VCKP22	14BE	25VATP22,

Tube Type	Basing	Replacement	Tube Type	Basing	Replacement
		25VDAP22, 25VDEP22, 25VDKP22, 25VDXP22			25VCZP22, 25VDCP22, 25VDRP22, 25VEBP22, 25VEDP22, 25VEHP22, 25VEXP22, 26DP22, 26KP22
25VCMP22	14BE	25VBYP22, 25VCDP22, 25VCTP22, 25VDFP22	25VCXP22	14BE	25VCTP22, 25VCZP22, 25VDAP22, 25VDXP22
25VCNP22	14BE	25VACP22, 25VCZP22, 25VDAP22, 25VDXP22, 25VEBP22	25VCYP22	14BE	25VBNP22, 25VBRP22[1], 25VCBP22, 25VCFP22, 25VCHP22, 25VCRP22, 25VEBP22
25CQP22	14BE	25VAZP22[1], 25VBGP22[1], 25VBNP22, 25VBRP22[1], 25VCBP22, 25VCFP22, 25VCUP22, 25VEBP22	25VCZP22	14BE	25VACP22, 25VBWP22, 25VCNP22, 25VDCP22, 25VDMP22, 25VDRP22, 25VDXP22, 25VEBP22, 25VEDP22, 25VEHP22, 25VEXP22, 25VFAP22, 25VFGP22
25VCRP22	14BE	25VAZP22[1], 25VBNP22, 25VBRP22[1], 25VCBP22, 25VCFP22[1], 25VCHP22, 25VCYP22, 25VEBP22	25VDAP22	14BE	25VCKP22, 25VDEP22, 25VDKP22, 25VDNP22, 25VDXP22
25VCSP22	14BE	25VAXP22, 25VBCP22, 25VDHP22, 26EP22	25VDBP22	14BE	25VDMP22, 25VDRP22, 25VEHP22, 25VEXP22, 25VFAP22
25VCTP22	14BE	25VCXP22	25VDCP22	14BE	25CZP22, 25VCUP22, 25VEBP22
25VCUP22	14BE	25VCNP22, 25VCZP22, 25VDCP22, 25VEBP22, 25VEDP22	25VDEP22	14BE	25VCKP22, 25VDAP22, 25VDXP22
25VCUP22	14BE	25VAWP22, 25VBWP22, 25VCEP22, 25VCNP22, 25VCZP22, 25VDCP22, 25VDRP22, 25VEBP22, 25VEDP22, 25VEHP22, 25VEXP22, 25VFAP22	25VDFP22	14BE	25VBEP22, 25VCMP22, 25VCTP22, 25VCXP22
25VCWP22	14BE	25VAWP22, 25VBZP22, 25VCEP22,	25VDGP22	14BE	25VBCP22, 26EP22
			25VDHP22	14BE	

Tube Type	Basing	Replacement
25VDJP22	14BE	25VATP22, 25VBXP22
25VDKP22	14BE	25VCKP22, 25VDAP22, 25VDXP22
25VDMP22	14BE	25VCZP22, 25VDBP22, 25VDNP22, 25VDRP22, 25VDSP22, 25VDWP22, 25VEDP22, 25VEHP22, 25VEXP22, 25VFAP22
25VDNP22	14BE	25VDMP22, 25VDRP22 25VEXP22, 25VFAP22
25VDRP22	14BE	25VCZP22, 25VDBP22, 25VDMP22, 25VDNP22, 25VDSP22, 25VDWP22, 25VEDP22, 25VEHP22, 25VEXP22, 25VFAP22
25VDSP22	14BE	25VAWP22, 25VBWP22, 25VCEP22, 25VCNP22, 25VCUP22, 25VCZP22, 25VDCP22, 25VDRP22, 25VEBP22, 25VEDP22, 25VEXP22
25VDWP22	14BE	25VDMP22, 25VDRP22, 25VEXP22, 25VFAP22
25VDXP22	14BE	25VATP22, 25VCKP22, 25VDAP22, 25VDBP22, 25VDEP22, 25VDKP22, 25VDMP22, 25VDNP22, 25VEDP22

Tube Type	Basing	Replacement
25VEBP22	14BE	25VCZP22, 25VDMP22
25VECP22	14BE	
25VEDP22	14BE	25VATP22, 25VAWP22, 25VBWP22, 25VCEP22, 25VCUP22, 25VCZP22, 25VDMP22, 25VDRP22, 25VDSP22, 25VEHP22, 25VEXP22, 25VFAP22
25VEHP22	14BE	25VAWP22, 25VBWP22, 25VCEP22, 25VDBP22, 25VDMP22, 25VDRP22, 25VEDP22, 25VEXP22, 25VFAP22
25VEKP22	14BP	
25VEMP22	13K	25VEQP22, 25VESP22, 25VETP22, 25VEWP22, 25VFBP22
25VEQP22	13K	25VEMP22, 25VESP22, 25VEWP22, 25VFBP22
25VERP22	14BE	
25VESP22	13K	25VEMP22, 25VEQP22, 25VETP22, 25VEWP22, 25VFBP22
25VETP22	13K	25VEMP22, 25VEQP22, 25VESP22, 25VEWP22, 25VFBP22
25VEUP22	13K	
25VEWP22	13K	25VEMP22, 25VEQP22, 25VESP22, 25VETP22, 25VFBP22, 25VFKP22
25VEXP22	14BE	25VCUP22, 25VCZP22,

Tube Type	Basing	Replacement	Tube Type	Basing	Replacement
		25VDBP22, 25VDMP22, 25VDNP22, 25VDRP22, 25VDSP22, 25VDWP22, 25VEDP22, 25VEHP22, 25VFAP22	25XP22	14BE	23VAHP22, 23VALP22, 23VANP22, 23VARP22, 25ABP22, 25BGP22, 25GP22A
25VEYP22	13L		25YP22	14BE	25BP22, A
25VEZP22	14BE		25ZP22	14BE	23VALP22, 23VANP22, 23VARP22
25VFAP22	14BE	25VCUP22, 25VCZP22, 25VDBP22, 25VDMP22, 25VDNP22, 25VDRP22, 25VDSP22, 25VDWP22, 25VEDP22, 25VEHP22, 25VEXP22	26AP22	14BE	25VABP22, 25VCKP22, 25VDXP22
			26DP22	14BE	25VBZP22, 25VCUP22, 25VCWP22, 25VCZP22, 25VDCP22
			26EP22	14BE	25VAXP22, 25VCSP22, 25VDGP22, 25VDHP22
25VFBP22	13K	25VEMP22, 25VEQP22, 25VESP22, 25VETP22, 25VEWP22	26FP22	14BE	25VABP22, 25VAEP22, 25VBZP22, 25VCDP22, 25VCUP22, 25VCZP22, 25VDXP22, 26DP22
25VFEP22	13L				
25VFGP22	14BE	25VBWP22, 25VCNP22 25VCZP22, 25VDCP22, 25VDRP22, 25VEBP22, 25VEDP22, 25VEHP22, 25VEXP22	26GP22	14BE	25VBZP22, 25VCUP22, 25VCWP22, 25VDCP22, 26DP22
			26HP22	14BE	25VAGP22, 25VBEP22, 25VBKP22, 25VBYP22, 25VCTP22, 25VCXP22, 25VDFP22
25VFJP22	13L				
25VFKP22	13K	25VEMP22, 25VESP22, 25VETP22, 25VEWP22, 25VFBP22	26KP22	14BE	25VBZP22, 25VCUP22, 25VCWP22, 25VCZP22, 26DP22
25VFMP22	13K				
25VFNP22	13L		27ABP4	8HR	27ADP4, 27AGP4, 27AFP4[1]
25VFSP22	13L		27ACP4	12L	27YP4
25VFZP22	13L		27ADP4	8HR	27AFP4[1]
25VFTP22	13K		27AEP4	8HR	27ZP4[1]
25VGAP22	13L		27AFP4	8HR	27ADP4[1]
25WP22	14BE	23VABP22, 23VALP22, 23VANP22, 23VARP22, 25ABP22, 25ANP22	27AGP4	8HR	27ABP4, 27ADP4, 27AFP4[1]
			27AP4	12M	

Tube Type	Basing	Replacement
27EP4	12D	27GP4
27GP4	12D	27EP4
27LP4	12N	
27MP4	12D	
27NP4	12N	27RP4
27RP4	12N	27NP4, 27RP4A*
27RP4A	12N	27NP4, 27RP4*
27SP4	12L	27UP4*, 27VP4*, 27XP4*
27UP4	12L	27SP4, 27VP4*, 27XP4*
27VP4	12L	27XP4
27WP4	12AJ	
27XP4	12L	
27YP4	12L	27ACP4
27ZP4	8HR	27AEP4[1]
30BP4	12D	
230ACB4	7GR	9AGP4, 9YP4
230RB4	7GR	9WP4
230TB4	7GR	9WP4
230ZB4	7GR	9YP4
310AVB4	7GR	12CNP4
320GB22	14BH	12DCP22
370AB22	14BH	14VADP22, 15NP22
370CB22	14BH	14VAMP22, 15AEP22, 15NP22
370CR22	14BH	15NP22
400AFB4A	8HR	16BGP4
400CVB22	14BH	16CYP22
440ACB4	8HR	16VAJP4, 17ESP4
440HB4	8HR	17EMP4, 17ESP4
440VB4	8HR	17EWP4
470AB4	8HR	19AVP4
470ACB4	8HR	19AYP4
470CB4	8HR	19AVP4
470DMB22	14BH	17VAWP22
490AB22	14BE	18VAHP22[2], 19EXP22[2], 19GYP22[2]
490ACB22	14BE	18VAHP22[2], 19EXP22[2], 19GYP22[2]
490ADB22	14BE	18VAHP22[2], 19EXP22[2], 19GYP22[2]
490AEB22	14BE	18VAHP22[2], 19EYP22[2], 19GWP22[2]
490AFB22	14BE	18VAHP22[2], 19EYP22[2], 19GWP22[2]
490AGB22	14BE	18VAHP22[2], 19EYP22[2], 19GWP22[2]

Tube Type	Basing	Replacement
490AHB22	14BE	18VAHP22, 19EXP22, 19GYP22[2]
490AHB22A	14BE	18VAHP22, 19EXP22[2], 19GVP22[2]
490AJB22	14BE	18VAHP22, 19EYP22, 19GWP22
490AJB22A	14BE	18VAHP22, 19EYP22, 19GWP22
490AKB22	14BE	18VAHP22[2], 19EYP22[2], 19GVP22[2]
490ALB22	14BE	18VAHP22[2], 19EYP22[2], 19GVP22[2]
490AMB22	14BE	18VAHP22[2], 18VAMP22, 19EXP22[2], 19GVP22[2]
490ANB22	14BE	18VAHP22[2], 19EXP22[2], 19GVP22[2]
490ARB22	14BE	18VAHP22[2], 19EYP22[2], 19GWP22[2]
490ASB22	14BE	18VAHP22, 19EYP22[2], 19GWP22
490BAB22	14BE	18VAHP22, 19GVP22, 19GXP22
490BCB22	14BE	18VAHP22, 19GWP22, 19EYP22
490BDB22	14BE	18VAHP22, 19GWP22[2], 19GYP22[2]
490BGB22	14BE	18VAHP22, 19GVP22, 19EP22
490BHB22	14BE	18VAHP22, 19EXP22, 19GVP22
490BKB22	14BE	18VAKP22
490BNB22	14BH	19JWP22
490BRB22	14BE	18VAHP22, 19EYP22, 19GWP22
490BUB22	14BE	18VAKP22
490BVB22	14BH	19JWP22
490BXB22	14BH	19JWP22
490CB22	14BE	19EXP22[2], 19GVP22[2]
490CHB22	14BE	18VAHP22
490CUB22	14BE	18VAHP22
490DB22	14BE	18VAHP22, 19EXP22[2], 19GVP22[2]
490EB22	14BE	18VAHP22[2], 19EXP22[2], 19GVP22[2]
490EB22A	14BE	18VAHP22[2],

Tube Type	Basing	Replacement
		19EXP22[2], 19GVP22[2]
490FB22	14BE	18VAHP22[2], 19EXP22[2], 19GVP22[2]
490GB22	14BE	18VAHP22[2], 19EXP22[2], 19GVP22[2]
490HB22	14BE	18VAHP22[2], 19EXP22, 19GVP22
490JB22	14BE	18VAHP22[2], 19EXP22, 19GVP22
490JB22A	14BE	18VAHP22[2], 19EXP22, 19GVP22
490KB22	14BE	18VAHP22[2], 19EXP22[2], 19GVP22
490KB22A	14BE	18VAHP22[2], 19EXP22[2], 19GVP22[2]
490LB22	14BE	18VAHP22[2], 19EXP22[2], 19GVP22[2]
490MB22	14BE	18VAHP22[2], 19EXP22[2], 19GVP22[2]
490NB22	14BE	18VAHP22, 19EYP22[2], 19GWP22[2]
490RB22	14BE	18VAHP22, 19EYP22[2], 19GWP22[2]
490SB22	14BE	18VAHP22, 19EYP22[2], 19GWP22[2]
490TB22	14BE	18VAHP22, 19EYP22[2], 19GWP22[2]
490UB22	14BE	18VAHP22[2], 19EXP22[2], 19GVP22[2]
490VB22	14BE	18VAHP22[2], 19EXP22[2], 19GVP22[2]
490WB22	14BE	18VAHP22[2], 19EYP22[2], 19GWP22[2]
490XB22	14BE	18VAHP22[2], 19EYP22[2], 19GWP22[2]
490YB22	14BE	18VAHP22[2], 19EYP22[2], 19GWP22[2]
490ZB22	14BE	18VAHP22[2], 19EYP22[2], 19GWP22[2]
500KB4	8HR	20TP4
510ELB22	14BE	19VBRP22
510ERB22	14BE	19VBRP22
A31-265W	7GR	12VAMP4
A44-18W	8HR	19VCUP4
A49-12X	14BE	18VAHP22, 19GWP22
A55-13X	14BE	20VAGP22, 22JP22
A66-501X	14BQ	24VABP22
AW43-80	12AJ	17BTP4
AW43-88	8HR	17CVP4
AW53-80	12AJ	21CLP4
AW53-88	8HR	21DKP4

LOW E_{g2}

Type	Voltage	Type	Voltage	Type	Voltage	Type	Voltage
8DP4	150V	12CNP4	200V	15VANP4	170V	17CXP4	50V
9ACP4	100V	12CQP4	40V	16ATP4	50V	17DQP4	50V
9AGP4	100V	12CSP4	100V	16AVP4	35V	17EHP4	50V
9AMP4	130V	12CTP4	100V	16AWP4	150V	17ELP4	50V
9QP4, A	200V	12CUP4	50V	16AZP4	150V	17EMP4	50V
9TP4	50V	12CVP4	100V	16BAP4	50V	17EWP4	30V
9UP4	100V	12CWP4	140V	16BCP4	35V	18VALP22	100V
9VADP4	100V	12CXP4	100V	16BEP4	50V	18VBGP22	100V
9VAHP4	130V	12CZP4	100V	16BNP4	50V	19ACP4	50V
9VAJP4	90V	12DEP4	100V	16BSP4	50V	19AEP4	100V
9VAKP4	130V	12DFP4	200V	16BUP4	100V	19AJP4	50V
9VALP4	130V	12DGP4	50V	16BXP4	35V	19BDP4	50V
9VARP4	90V	12DHP4	50V	16BYP4	100V	19BNP4	50V
9VASP4	120V	12DKP4	140V	16CFP4	140V	19BQP4	50V
9VATP4	90V	12DQP4	50V	16CHP4	30V	19CDP4	50V
9VAUP4	120V	12VABP4	50V	16CNP4	100V	19CFP4	50V
9VAWP4	90V	12VAEP4	100V	16CQP4	140V	19CHP4	50V
9VAZP4	100V	12VAFP4	130V	16CWP4	100V	19CKP4	50V
9VP4	100V	12VAMP4	130V	16CWP4A	140V	19CLP4	35V
9WP4	100V	12VAWP4	130V	16CXP4	100V	19CMP4	30V
9YP4	100V	12VAXP4	150V	16DCP4A	140V	19CQP4	50V
10ARP4	140V	12VAZP4	100V	16VABP4	50V	19CUP4	65V
10ASP4	100V	12VBCP4	140V	16VADP4	130V	19CVP4	50V
10AVP4	90V	12VBEP4	140V	16VAKP22	100V	19CXP4	45V
10VACP4	100V	12VBFP4	130V	16VAQP4	50V	19DBP4	40V
10VAEP4	100V	12VBGP4	130V	16VARP4	50V	19DFP4	65V
11AP4	150V	12VBHP4	130V	16VBJP4	130V	19DHP4	50V
11BP4	150V	12VBLP4	120V	16VBKP4	130V	19DLP4	50V
11DP4	50V	12VBMP4	110V	16VBNP4	130V	19DSP4	50V
11GP4	135V	12VBNP4	90V	16VBQP4	135V	19DUP4	50V
11JP4	50V	12VBQP4	130V	16VBRP4	130V	19DVP4	150V
11KP4	50V	12VBRP4	130V	16VBTP4	130V	19DYP4	50V
11HP4	150V	12VBWP4	140V	16VBWP4	130V	19DZP4	150V
11MP4	135V	12VBXP4	140V	16VBXP4	130V	19EAP4	50V
11QP4	100V	12VCAP4	130V	16VBYP4	130V	19ECP4	150V
11RP4	140V	12VCBP4	120V	16VBZP4	150V	19EFP4	50V
11UP4	140V	12CGP4	120V	16VCAP4	130V	19EGP4	50V
12BEP4	30V	12VCJP4	130V	16VCBP4	130V	19EJP4	30V
12BFP4	200V	12VCKP4	120V	16VCDP4	130V	19EKP4	45V
12BGP4	50V	12VCLP4	120V	16VCEP4	130V	19ENP4	50V
12BKP4	50V	13AP4	50V	16VCFP4	130V	19ESP4	50V
12BLP4	30V	13DP4	50V	16VCGP4	50V	19ETP4	50V
12BMP4	140V	13VARP4	110V	16VCHP4	50V	19EZP4	45V
12BNP4	250V	13VASP4	100V	16VCJP4	130V	19FBP4	50V
12BQP4	50V	13VAZP4	130V	16VCRP4	130V	19FDP4	130V
12BRP4	30V	14ACP4	125V	16VCSP4	135V	19FEP4	30V
12BTP4	50V	14AEP4	110V	16VCWP4	130V	19FQP4	50V
12BUP4	50V	14AJP4	250V	16VCXP4	130V	19GHP4	50V
12BVP4	50V	14ARP4	50V	16VCYP4	150V	19GMP4	50V
12BWP4	35V	14AUP4	50V	16VCZP4	150V	19GQP4	50V
12BZP4	100V	14AWP4	50V	17BMP4	110V	19GTP4	50V
12CBP4	30V	14VARP4	130V	17BNP4	110V	19HAP4	50V
12CDP4	140V	15ADP4	50V	17CMP4	50V	19HGP4	150V
12CEP4	100V	15JP4	50V	17CNP4	50V	19VAHP4	130V
12CFP4	200V	15VAJP4	140V	17CRP4	50V	19VCLP4	50V

LOW E_{g2}

Type	Voltage	Type	Voltage	Type	Voltage	Type	Voltage
19VCMP4	50V	20RP4	50V	23AWP4	50V	23FWP4	50V
19VCAP22	100V	20SP4	30V	23BGP4	50V	23GHP4	200V
19VEMP4	150V	20YP4	50V	23BHP4	50V	23GJP4	50V
19VERP4	135V	20ZP4	50V	23BJP4	50V	23GRP4	30V
19VFDP4	130V	21CGP4	110V	23BKP4	50V	23GUP4	30V
19VFEP4	130V	21CHP4	110V	23BLP4	50V	23GVP4	45V
19VFGP4	150V	21CXP4	50V	23DAP4	50V	23GWP4	50V
19VFYP4	50V	21DSP4	50V	23DBP4	50V	23GYP4	50V
19VFZP4	50V	21FMP4	50V	23DCP4	50V	23HAP4	50V
19VFTP4	130V	21FUP4	50V	23DLP4	50V	23HKP4	150V
19VGAP4	50V	21FYP4	50V	23DNP4	35V	23HRP4	30V
19VGSP4	135V	21GAP4	30V	23DSP4	65V	23HUP4, A	30V
19VGUP4	130V	21GBP4	50V	23DWP4	200V	23JLP4	30V
19VGXP4	130V	21GEP4	50V	23ECP4	35V	23JRP4	30V
19VGYP4	130V	21GHP4	30V	23EFP4	50V	23JFP4	50V
19VHEP4	130V	21GKP4	50V	23ENP4	50V	23JGP4	30V
19VHGP4	130V	21GSP4	50V	23EP4	50V	23JP4	50V
19VHUP4	150V	21GTP4	50V	23EYP4	35V	23NP4	50V
19VJAP4	130V	22VARP4	50V	23EZP4	50V	23ZP4	50V
19VJGP4	150V	22VASP4	50V	23FBP4	50V	24AJP4	50V
19VUP4	130V	22VBAP4	150V	23FCP4	50V	24ATP4	50V
20ABP4	50V	22VBCP4	140V	23FDP4	50V	24BAP4	50V
20ADP4	35V	22VBDP4	150V	23FEP4	50V	25HP4	50V
20AHP4	150V	23ANP4	50V	23FHP4	50V	25VBZP22	200V
20AZP4	30V	23ATP4	50V	23FRP4	50V		

ODD FILAMENT VOLTAGES

Type	Voltage	Type	Voltage	Type	Voltage	Type	Voltage
5VACP4	12.0V	10AFP4	11.0V	12VBQP	11.0V	16VCAP4	11.0V
5VADP4	12.0V	10VAGP4	11.0V	12VBRP4	11.0V	16VCBP4	11.0V
9ACP4	12.0V	11NP4	11.0V	12VBSP4	11.0V	16VCDP4	11.0V
9AGP4	12.0V	11QP4	12.6V	12VBWP4	12.0V	16VCHP4	4.2V
9QP4,A	4.7V	11WP22	13.8V	12VCAP4	11.0V	16VCXP4	11.0V
9UP4	12.6V	12AP4	2.5V	12VCBP4	11.0V	17CDP4	8.4V
9VADP4	12.0V	12BFP4	4.2V	12VCFP4	11.0V	17DAP4	2.68V
9VAHP4	12.0V	12BJP4	4.2V	12VCGP4	11.0V	17DEP4	2.35V
9VAJP4	11.0V	12BRP4	12.6V	12VCJP4	11.0V	17DRP4	2.68V
9VAKP4	11.0V	12BTP4	12.6V	12VCKP4	11.0V	19ABP4	2.68V
9VALP4	11.0V	12BVP4	12.6V	12VCLP4	11.0V	19AEP4	12.6V
9VANP4	11.0V	12BZP4	12.0V	13VAJP4	11.0V	19BUP4	2.2V
9VARP4	11.0V	12CEP4	12.6V	13VANP4	11.0V	19FTP4	11.0V
9VASP4	11.0V	12CFP4	4.2V	13VAQP4	12.0V	19FYP4	4.2V
9VATP4	11.0V	12CNP4	4.2V	13VARP4	12.0V	19VDAP4	4.2V
9VAUP4	11.0V	12CP4	2.5V	13VASP4	11.0V	19VGUP4	11.0V
9VAWP4	11.0V	12CUP4	4.2V	13VAZP4	11.0V	19VJAP4	11.0V
9VAZP4	12.0V	12CVP4	12.0V	14ATP4	8.4V	21EAP4	2.35V
9VP4	12.6V	12CXP4	12.6V	15VANP, A	11.0V	21EVP4	2.68V
9WP4	12.0V	12CZP4	12.6V	16CNP4	12.0V	22VBCP4	11.0V
9XP4	12.6V	12VBFP4	12.0V	16CXP4	12.0V	23BZP4	8.4V
9YP4	12.6V	12VBGP4	12.0V	16VADP4	11.0V	23CAP4	8.4V
10ADP4	8.4V	12VBLY4	12.0V	16VBWP4	11.0V	23EHP4	8.4V
10AVP4	12.0V	12VBMP	12.0V	16VBXP4	11.0V	24AVP4	2.35V
10VAEP4	11.0V	12VBNP4	11.0V	16VBYP4	11.0V		

Industrial Substitutes for Receiving Tubes

In this section are those American receiving tubes that can be replaced by industrial types. The receiving tubes are listed in the left-hand column and their industrial substitutes in the right-hand column. Each tube listed has one or more substitutes. If a tube type does not appear in the listing, an industrial substitute is not recommended.

This substitution list should be used in one direction only—that is, an industrial type to replace a standard type. If the equipment is already designed for an industrial tube, a standard receiving tube will not usually work as efficiently or as long as the original.

For the basing diagram of tubes in this section, refer to Section 1 to obtain the code and then to Section 7 for the basing diagram.

Substitutes marked with an asterisk (*) should be used only when the filament of the original tube is wired in a parallel circuit.

Tube Type	Replacement	Tube Type	Replacement
0A2	0A2WA, 6073, 6626	6AT6	6066
0A4G	1267, WTT132	6AU6	6AU6WA, 6AU6WB, 6136
0B2	0B2WA, 6074, 6627	6AV6	6066
0C3	0C3W, VR105W, WT269	6BA5	5638
0D3	0D3W, VR150W, WT294	6BA6	6BA6W, 6BA6WA, 5749,
0Z4	1003, WTT114		6660, 7496
0Z4A	1003	6BE6	6BE6W, 5750, 7502*
1F4	2101	6BH6	6265*, 6661, 7693
1R4	1294	6BJ6	6662, 7694
1R5	1R5WA	6BL8	7643*
1T4	1T4WA	6BQ5	7320
1U4	1U4WA, 5910	6BR7	6059
1U5	1U5WA	6BW6	6061
2A3	2A3W, 5930	6C4	6C4W, 6C4WA, 6100, 6135*
2A6	1659	6C5	WT390
2X2	2B21, 879	6C6	1221, 1223, 7700, WTT131
2X2A	2B21	6CB6	6676, 7732
3B4	3B4WA	6CH6	6132, 7499
3B7	1291	6CL6	2014, 6197, 6297, 6677
3D6	1299	6CQ6	6065
3Q5GT	WT389	6CW4	7895
3V4	3V4WA	6CY5	7717, 8113
5R4GY	5R4WGA, WGB, WGY,	6DB6	6954
	WGYA, 274B	6DJ8	6922*
5U4G	5U4WG, WGB, 5931,	6DK6	8136
	WTT135	6DS4	7895
5V4G	274	6F6	1611, 1621
5Y3GT	5Y3WGT, WGTA, WGTB,	6G6G	WTT130
	6087, 6106, 6853,	6GE8	7734
	WTT202	6H6	6H6WGT, WTT103, WT261
5Z3	1275, WT270X	6J4	6J4W, WA, 8532
5Z4	6087	6J5	6J5WGT, WTT129
6AB4	6664	6J6	6J6W, 6J6WA, 5964, 6030,
6AB7	1853		6045*, 6099, 6101, 6927*
6AC7	6AC7W, 6AC7WA, 6AC7Y,	6J7	1223, 1620, 7000
	1852, 6134	6K5	6K5WGT
6AG5	6AG5WA, 6186	6K7	5732
6AG7	6AG7W	6K8	WTT128
6AH6	6AH6WA, 6485	6L6	6L6W, WA, WGA, WGB,
6AJ5	7755		WGT, 1622, 5932, WT6
6AK5	6AK5W, WA, WB, 403A,	6L7	1612, 1620
	1220, 5654, 5591*,	6N7	5694
	6096, 6968	6N7GT	WTT125
6AL5	6AL5W, 5726, 6058, 6097,	6Q5G	884, WT245
	6663, 7631, D27	6Q7	6118
6AM5	6516	6SA7	6SA7WGT, 5961
6AM6	6064, 7498	6SC7	1655
6AN5	6AN5WA	6SG7	6006
6AQ5	6AQ5W, 6005, 6095, 6669	6SJ7	6SJ7W, 6SJ7WGT,
6AR6	6AR6WA, 6098, 6384, 7756		6SJ7WGTY, 5693, WTT122
6AS6	6AS6W, 409A, 5725,	6SK7	6SK7W, 6SK7WA,
	6187*, 7752		6SK7WGT, 6137
6AS7G	6AS7GYB, 6080WA,	6SL7	6SL7W, 6SL7WGT, 5691*,
	6080WB, 6520		6113

Tube Type	Replacement
6SN7	6SN7W, 6SN7WGT, 6SN7WGTA, 5692
6SQ7	6SQ7W
6SU7	6SU7WGT, 6188
6U6	6U6WGT
6U8	1252, 6678, 7731
6V6	5871, 7184, WTT123
6X4	6X4W, WA, 6063, 6202, WTT100
6X5	6X5W, WGT, 5852*, WT308
6Y7G	1635
6Z4	WT263
7A6	5679
7AB7	1204
7AJ7	1273
7C4	1203, 1203A
7E5	1201
7F8	7F8W
7G7	1232
7G8	1206
7K7	WTT124
7Y4	1274*
12A6	12A6GTY, 5659
12AT7	12AT7WA, 12AT7WB, 6060, 6201, 6671, 6679, 7492, 7728, A2900
12AU7	12AU7W, WA, 5814*, A, 5814WA*, 5963, 6067, 6189, 6680, 7316, 7489, 7730

Tube Type	Replacement
12AX7	12AX7WA, 5751*, 5751WA*, 6057, 6681, 7494, 7729
12AY7	6072*
12BH7	6913
12BR7	8447
12BY7	7733, 8448
12C8	1664, 5660
12J5	12J5WGT
12L6GT	1632*
12L8GT	1644
12SC7	1634
12SK7	5661
12SL7GT	2C52*
12Z3	H250
14C7	1280
14GT8	7724
25B6G	5824
25L6GT	6046
25W6GT	6046
25Z6	25Z6WGT
26E6G	26E6WG, 26E6WGB
26Z5	26Z5W
28D7	28D7W, 1238
50B5	WTT126
80	213B, RE1, WT270
81	RE2
83	WT301
117N7GT	WTT115
117Z6GT	WT377
807	807W, 5933, WA, 8018

§ May not work in all circuits.   * Parallel-filament circuits.

Communications and
Special-Purpose Tubes

This section lists communications and special-purpose tubes. The tubes to be replaced are listed in the left-hand column and the recommended substitutes in the right-hand column.

The listing of a certain tube type as a substitute for another one does not necessarily mean the reverse is true. Always refer to the left-hand column for the original tube number. Then find the substitute in the right-hand column.

Where the basing code is available, it is given in the second column. Use this number and refer to Section 7 for the pin connections.

Substitutes marked with an asterisk (*) should be used only when the filament of the original tube is wired in a parallel circuit.

Tube Type	Basing	Replacement
RE1	4C	80
2-15A/15R		4B30, 15R, 8022
2A3W	4D	5930
2B21	4AB	2X2A
2C21	7BH	1642
2C22	4AM	7193
2C51	8CJ	2C51W*, 396A, 1219, 5670*, 5670WA*, 6185, 6385*
2C51W	8CJ	1219, 5670, 5670WA, 6185
2D21	7BN	2D21W, 5727
2D21W	7BN	5727
2RA3		213, 213A
2RA5		205
2RA6		206, 619
2RA15		203, 215
RE2		81
EL3B	4CQ	6013
EL3C		4B24, 6484
4-125A	5BK	4D21, 4D21A, 6155
4-250A		4-250/5D22, 5D22, 6156
SN4		1D21, 631P1
5R4WGA	5T	5R4WGB, 5R4WGY, 5R4WGYA
5R4WGB	5T	5R4WGYA
5R4WGY	5T	5R4WGA, 5R4WGB, 5R4WGYA
5R4WGYA	5T	5R4WGB
5U4WG	5T	5U4WGB, 5931
5U4WGB	5T	5931
5Y3WGT	5T	5Y3WGTA, 5Y3WGTB, 6087, 6106, 6853
5Y3WGTA	5T	5Y3WGTB, 6087, 6106, 6853
5Y3WGTB	5T	5Y3WGTA, 6087, 6106, 6853
ELC5F14		6278
6AC7W	8N	6AC7WA, 6134
6AC7WA	8N	6AC7W, 6134
6AG5WA	7BD	6186
6AK5W	7BD	6AK5WB, 5654
6AL5W	6BT	5726, 6097
6AQ5W	7BZ	6005, 6095
6AR6WA	6BQ	6098
6AS6W	7CM	5725, 6187
6AS7GYB	8BD	6080, 6080WA, 6080WB
6AU6WA	7BK	6AU6WB, 6136
6AU6WB	7BK	6136
6BA6W	7BK	5749
6BE6W	7CH	5750
6C4W	6BG	6C4WA, 6100, 6135*
6C4WA	6BG	6100, 6135*
6J6W	7BF	6J6WA, 6099, 6101
6J6WA	7BF	6099, 6101
6L6W	7AC	6L6WA, 6L6WGA, 6L6WGB, 5932
6L6WA	7AC	6L6WGA, 6L6WGB, 5932
6L6WGA	7AC	6L6WGB, 5932
6L6WGB	7AC	5881
6L6WGT	7AC	5932
6Q5G	6Q	884, 884W
6SJ7W	8N	6SJ7WGT, 6SJ7WGTY
6SJ7WGT	8N	6SJ7W, 6SJ7WGTY
6SJ7WGTY	8N	6SJ7W, 6SJ7WGT
6SK7W	8N	6SK7WA, 6SK7WGT
6SK7WA	8N	6SK7W, 6SK7WGT
6SK7WGT	8N	6SK7W, 6SK7WA
6SL7W	8BD	6SL7WGT, 6113
6SL7WGT	8BD	6SL7W, 6113
6SN7W	8BD	6SN7WGT, 6SN7WGTA
6SN7WGT	8BD	6SN7W, 6SN7WGTA
6SN7WGTA	8BD	6SN7W, 6SN7WGT
6SU7WGT	8BD	6188
6X4W	5BS	6X4WA
6X5W	6S	6X5WGT
6X5WGT	6S	6X5W
EL6B		618, 618P, 5892
WT6	7AC	6L6
12AT7WA	9A	6201
12AT7WB	9A	6201
12AU7WA	9A	6189
12AX7WA	9A	5721, 6057, 7494, 7729
D27	6BT	6AL5
RK28		803
31Z		1231Z
RK31		830B
TE36		6754
RK39	5AW	807
TE40	8N	6888
HZ50	6G	12Z3
RK57		805
RK58		838
T60		8005
HY61	5AW	807
WTT100	5BS	6X4
WTT102	5T	5Y3GT
WTT103	7Q	6H6
CK108	6F	77
HY113		HY123
WTT114	4R	0Z4
HY115		HY145

Tube Type	Basing	Replacement
WTT115	8AV	117N7GT
WTT117		5557
WTT118		105
WTT119		172
WTT122	8N	6SJ7
HY123		HY113
WTT123	7AC	6V6
WTT124	8BF	7K7
HF125		203H
HY125		HY155
WTT125	8B	6N7GT
WTT126	7BZ	50B5
WTT127		833A
WTT128	8K	6K8
WTT129	6Q	6J5GT
WTT130	7S	6G6G
WTT131	6F	6C6
WTT132	4V	0A4G
WTT135	5T	5U4G
HY145		HY115
WTT149		172
VR150W	4AJ	0D3W
HY155		HY125
WT210-0001	7BN	2D21
WT210-0003	6Q	884
WT210-0004	6BS	2050
WT210-0006	7Q	6H6
WT210-0009	5D	6Z4
WT210-0011	4AJ	0C3
WT210-0012	4C	80
WT210-0013	4C	5Z3
WT210-0018	4AJ	0D3
WT210-0019	4C	83
WT210-0021	6S	6X5
WT210-0025	7Q	117Z6GT
WT210-0028	7AP	3Q5GT
WT210-0029	6Q	6C5
WT210-0037	8AO	117L7/M7GT
WT210-0040	5BS	6X4
WT210-0042	5T	5Y3GT
WT210-0048	5T	5U4G
WT210-0060	4R	0Z4
WT210-0062		5557
WT210-0069		5557
WT210-0081	8N	6SJ7
WT210-0082	7AC	6V6
WT210-0083	8BF	7K7
WT210-0084	8B	6N7
WT210-0085	7BZ	50B5
WT210-0087	8K	6K8
WT210-0088	6Q	6J5
WT210-0089	7S	6G6G
WT210-0090	6F	6C6

Tube Type	Basing	Replacement
WT210-0091	4V	0A4G
213B	4C	80
UV216	4B	81
UX216B	4B	81
WT245	6Q	884
WT246	6BS	2050
H250	6F	6C6
259A		259B
259B		259A
WT261	7Q	6H6
WT263	5D	6Z4
264		864
WT269	4AJ	0C3
WT270	4C	80
WT270X	5T	5Z3
274	5L	5V4G
274B	5T	5R4GY
WT294	4AJ	0D3
WT301	4C	83
WT308	6S	6X5GT
310A	6F	310B
310B	6F	310A
S340	3Z	5960
WT377	7Q	117Z6GT
WT389	7AP	3Q5GT
WT390	6Q	6C5
396A	8CJ	2C51, 2C51W*, 1219*, 5670*, 5670WA*, 6185, 6385*
398A		5603
401A		5590
403A	7BD	6AK5
403B		5591
404A	9X	5847
408A	7BD	6028
409A	7CM	6AS6
412A		6754
417A	9V	417B, 5842
420A		5755
421A	8BD	5998
423A	9BY	6140
WT606	7BN	2D21
WL630	6BS	2050
WL630A	6BS	2050
731A	7BD	6AK5
807	5AW	807W, 807WA, RK39, HY61, 5933, 5933WA, 8018
807W	5AW	807WA, 5933, 5933WA
807WA	5AW	807W, 5933, 5933WA
879	4AB	2X2

* Parallel-filament circuits.

Tube Type	Basing	Replacement	Tube Type	Basing	Replacement
884	6Q	884W, 6Q5G	1662	7BB	3A4
885	5A	2B4	1664	8E	12C8
932	4K	1229	1665	6BS	2050, 2050A, 2050W
CK1003	4R	0Z4A	1852	8N	6AC7
CK1009		CK1009A, BA	1853	8N	6AB7
C1106		6AZ6	2013	9A	6211
NU1106		6AZ6	2014	9BV	6CL6, 6197
1201	8BN	7E5, 1201A	2050	6BS	1657, 1665, 2050A, 2050W
1201A	8BN	7E5, 1201			
1203	4AH	7C4, 1203A	2050A	6BS	1657, 1665, 2050, 2050W
1203A	4AH	7C4, 1203			
1204	8BO	7AB7	2935A	4B	81
1206	8BV	7G8	3841	4C	80
1216	7BF	5844	3871	4D	50
1217	7CH	6BE6, 5915, 5915A, 7036	3872	4D	30
			3873	4K	32
1219	8CJ	2C51W, 5670, 5670WA, 6185, 6385*	3921	4D	45
			3924	5E	24A
			4465	5E	35
1221	6F	6C6	4610	5E	36
1223	7R	6J7, 1620, 7000	4611	5A	37
1225	7T	6L7	4612	5F	38
1229	4K	932	5517		1B48, CK1013
1231	8V	7V7	5556		PJ8
1231Z		31Z	5588		6161
1232	8V	7G7	5590	7BD	401A
1273	8V	7AJ7	5591	7BD	403B
1274	6S	7Y4*	5603	6BD	398A
1275	4C	5Z3	5654	7BD	6AK5W, 6AK5WB, 1220, 6096
1280	8V	14C7			
1282	8BJ	7W7	5659	7S	12A6
1288	7BE	3B7, 1291, 1292	5660	8E	12C8
1291	7BE	3B7, 1288, 1292	5661	8N	12SK7
1292	7BE	3B7, 1288, 1291	5667		889RA
1294	4AH	1R4	5670	8CJ	2C51W, 1219, 5670WA, 6185, 6385*
1299	6BA	3D6			
1381HQ	7BD	6AK5			
1603	6F	6C6, 7700	5687	9H	5687WA
1611	7S	6F6	5721	9A	6057, 7494, 7729
1612	7T	6L7	5725	7CM	6AS6W, 6187
1613	7S	6F6	5726	6BT	6AL5W, 6097
1614	7AC	6L6	5727	7BN	2D21W
1620	7R	6J7, 1223, 7000	5731	5BC	955
1621	7S	6F6	5742		PJ7
1622	7AC	6L6	5743		PJ21
1632	7S	12L6	5749	7BK	6BA6W
1634	8R	12SC7	5750	7CH	6BE6W
1642	7BH	2C21	5751	9A	5751WA
1644	8BU	12L8GT	5755	9J	420A
1649	8N	6AC7	5759		501R
1650	5BC	955	5762		7C24, 5762A
1655	8S	6SC7	5763	9K	6062
1657	6BS	2050, 2050A, 2050W	5767		6481
1659	6G	2A6	5771		356

Tube Type	Basing	Replacement	Tube Type	Basing	Replacement
5794		5794A, 6562	6134	8N	6AC7W, 6AC7WA
5794A		6562	6135	6BG	6C4WA*, 6100*
5814	9A	5814A, 5814WA	6136	7BK	6AU6WA, 6AU6WB
5814A	9A	5814WA	6146B		8298A
5824	7AC	25B6G	6155		4-125A, 4D21
5842	9V	417A, 417B	6161		5588
5844	7BF	1216	6166A		7007
5847	9X	404A	6185		2C51W, 1219, 5670, WA
5871	7AC	6V6GT			
5881	7AC	6L6WGB, 7581, 7581A	6186	7BD	6AG5WA
			6187	7CM	6AS6W, 5725*
5894		9903	6188	8BD	6SU7WGT
5910	6AR	1U4, 1U4WA	6189	9A	12AU7WA
5915	7CH	6BE6, 1217, 5915A, 7036	6197	9BV	2014
			6201	9A	12AT7WA, 12AT7WB
5915A	7CH	6BE6, 1217, 5915, 7036	6211	9A	2013
			6252		9910
5923		9904	6485	7BK	6AH6WA
5930	4D	2A3W	6582	9EJ	TE35
5931	5T	5U4WGB	6626	5BO	0A2WA, 6073
5932	7S	6L6WGA, 6L6WGB	6627	5BO	0B2WA, 6074
5933	5AW	807, 807W, 807WA, 5933WA	6660	7CC	6BA6, 6BA6W, 5749
			6661	7CM	6BH6
5933WA	5AW	807, 807W, 807WA, 5933	6662	7CM	6BJ6
			6663	6BT	6AL5, 6AL5W, 5726, 6058, 6097
5992	7AC	6V6GT*			
6005	7BZ	6AQ5W, 6095	6664	5CE	6AB4
6028	7BD	408A	6669	7BZ	6AQ5A, 6AQ5W, 6005, 6095
6058	6BT	6AL5W, 5726, 6097			
6063	5BS	6X4, 6X4W, 6X4WA	6676	7CM	6CB6
6073	5BO	0A2WA, 6626	6677	9BY	6CL6
6074	5BO	0B2WA, 6627	6678	9AE	6U8A
6075		9907	6679	9A	12AT7, 12AT7WA, 12AT7WB, 6201
6076		9907R			
6077		9906	6680	9A	12AU7A, 12AU7WA, 6189, 7730
6078		9906R			
6079		9908	6681	9A	12AX7, 12AX7WA, 5721, 6057, 7494, 7729
6080	8BD	6080WA, 6080WB			
6080WA	8BD	6080WB			
6080WB	8BD	6080WA	6754	9ET	TE36, 412A
6083		9909	6853	5T	5Y3WGT, 5Y3WGTA, 5Y3WGTB, 6087, 6106
6087	5L	5Y3WGTB, 6106, 6853			
			6888	8N	TE40
6095	7BZ	6AQ5W, 6005	6939	9HL	7645
6096	7BD	6AK5W, 5654	6968	7ED	6AK5
6097	6BT	6AL5W, 5726	6979		4X250B
6098	6BQ	6AR6WA	7000	7R	6J7, 1223, 1620
6099	7BF	6J6WA, 6101	7007		6166A
6100	6BG	6C4WA, 6135*	7025	9A	12AX7, 7025A
6101	7BF	6J6WA, 6099	7025A	9A	12AX7, 7025
6106	5T	5Y3WGT, 5Y3WGTA, 5Y3WGTB, 6853	7027	8HY	7027A
			7034		4X150A
6113	8BD	6SL7W, 6SL7WGT			

* Parallel-filament circuits.

Tube Type	Basing	Replacement	Tube Type	Basing	Replacement
7035		4X150D, 7609	7645	9HL	6939
7036	7CH	6BE6, 1217, 5915, 5915A	7700	6F	6C6, 1603
			7729	9A	12AX7WA, 5721, 6057, 7494
7054	9GK	8077			
7184	9CV	6V6	7730	9A	12AU7WA, 6189
7189	9CV	7189A	7752	7CM	6AS6
7247	9A	12DW7	7755	7BD	6AJ5
7408	7AC	6V6GT	7756	6BQ	6AR6
7494	9A	12AX7WA, 5721, 6057, 7729	7867	5BT	6EX6*
			8016	3C	1B3GT
7543	7BK	6AU6, 6AU6WA, 6AU6WB, 6136	8018	5AW	807
			8077	9GK	7054
7581	7AC	7581A			

Foreign Substitutes for American Types

This section lists foreign substitutes for American tubes. Refer to this section only after checking for an American substitute in Sections 1, 3, and 4.

American tubes are shown in the left-hand column; foreign equivalents are in the right-hand column. Only those American types which can be replaced with foreign brands have been included. For a list of foreign types with American equivalents, refer to Section 6.

For the basing diagram of the American tubes in this section, refer to Section 1 or 4 to obtain the basing code and then to Section 7 for the basing diagram.

Substitutes marked with an asterisk (*) should be used only when the filament of the original tube is wired in a parallel circuit. Those tubes marked with a section symbol (§) may not work in all circuits.

Tube Type	Replacement	Tube Type	Replacement
0A2	150C2, 150C4, M8223, STV 150/30	1X2A	DY80, R19
		2B35	6D1, EA50, T6D
0A3	KD21	2D21	20A3, E91N, EN91, M8204, PL21
0A4G	PL1267, Z300T		
0B2	108C1, M8224, STV108/30	2ER5	XC95, XC97
0C3	KD24	2FY5	XC95, XC97
0D3	150C3, KD25	2HA5	XC900
0E3	85A1	2J2	R20, U26, U49
0G3	85A2	3A4	DL93
1A3	1D13, DA90	3A5	DCC90
1A5G	DL31	3AJ8	XCH81
1A7GT	DK32, X14	3AL5	XAA91
1AB6	1C3, 1H35, DK96, X25	3AU6	XF94
1AC6	1C2, DK92, X18, X20	3B4	DL98, HD30
1AD4	DF62	3B5GT	DL33, N15, N16
1AF4	1F1, DF96, W25	3BH2	GY501
1AF5	1FD1, DAF96, ZD25	3BX6	XF80, XF85
1AH5	1FD1, DAF96, ZD25	3BY7	XF80, XF85
1AJ4	1F1, DF96, W25	3BZ6	3M-V7
1AM4	1F1, DF96, W25	3C4	1P1, DL96, N25
1AN5	DF97	3C5GT	DL33, N15, N16
1AQ5	1H33	3D6	DL29
1AR5	1FD1, DAF96, ZD25	3DK6	3M-R24
1AS5	DAF92*	3E5	1P1, DL96, N25
1B3GT	DY30, U41	3EH7	XF183, XF184
1BG2	DY51	3EJ7	XF183, XF184
1C5GT	DL35, DL36, N14	3ER5	YC95
1DN5	DAF92	3FX7	3D-HH13
1E3	DC80	3FY5	YC97
1F5G	KL35*	3HA5	LC900
1G3GT	DY30, U41	3Q4	DL95, N18
1H5GT	DAC32, HD14	3Q5GT	DL33, N15, N16
1J3	DY30, U41	3S4	1P10, DL92, N17
1K3	DY30, U41	3V4	1P11, DL94, N19
1L4	1F2, DF92	4BC8	4R-HH2
1M3	DM70, DM71, Y25	4BL8	5R-HP1, XCF80
1N3	DM71, DM70, Y25	4BS8	4R-HH2
1N5GT	DF33, Z14	4CM4	PC86
1Q5GT	DL35, DL36, N14	4EH7	LF183, YF183
1R5	1C1, DK91, X17, 1H33*	4EJ7	LF184, YF184
1R5SF	1H33	4ES8	4R-HH8, XCC189
1S2	1RK23, DY86, DY87	4GJ7	XCF801
1S2A	DY87	4GK5	PC95
1S4	DL91	4HA5	PC900
1S5	1FD9, DAF91, ZD17	4KN8	4R-HH8
1T2	R16, U37	5AR4	52KU, 53KU, 54KU, GZ30, GZ32, GZ33, GZ34, GZ37, R52, U54, U77
1T4	1F3, DF91, W17		
1T4SF	1F1, DF96, W25		
1T5GT	DL31		
1U4	DF904	5AW4	U54
1U5	DAF92	5AX4GT	U54
1V	AD	5BK7A	4R-HH2
1V6	DCF60	5CG4	OSW3107
1X2	DY80, R19	5EA8	XCF80
		5GJ7	LCF801

Tube Type	Replacement	Tube Type	Replacement
5HG8	LCF86	6AQ8	6L12, B719, ECC85
5J6	5M-HH3	6AS6	6F33, M8196
5T4	GZ31, U52	6AS7G	A1834, ECC230
5U4G	5Z10, GZ32, U52	6AT6	6BC32, DH77, EBC90, EBC91
5U8	XCF80	6AU4GT	6G-K17
5U9	LCF201	6AU6	EF94
5V4G	52KU, 53KU, 54KU, GZ30, GZ32, GZ33, GZ34, OSW3107, R52, U54	6AV4	6FX4*, EZ91
		6AV6	6BC32, DH77, EBC90, EBC91
		6AW6	EF190
5V9	LCH200	6B8	EBF32*
5W4	U50, U51	6BA6	6F31, EF93, M8101, PM04, W727
5X9	LCF200		
5Y3GT	U50, U52	6BC5	EF96
5Z4	52KU, 53KU, 54KU, GZ30, GZ32, GZ33, GZ34, OSW3107, R52, U54, U77	6BD7	EBC80, EBC81, 6LD13*
		6BE6	6H31, EK90, HM04, X77, X727
5Z4G	52KU, GZ30, R52, U77	6BE7	EQ80
6A6	B63	6BH5	EF81
6A8	PH4, X63	6BH6	E90F
6AB4	EC92	6BJ6	N78
6AB7	6F10, OSW2190, OSW2600	6BJ6	E99F
6AB8	63TP, ECL80, LN152	6BK6	6BC32, DH77, EBC90, EBC91
6AC7	6F10, OSW2190, OSW2600	6BK8	EF83
6AD8	6FD12, EBF80, EBF81, EBF89, WD709, ZD152	6BL8	6C16, ECF80, E80CF*
		6BM5	6L31, 6P9, EL90, N727
6AF3	EY88*	6BM8	6PL12, ECL82
6AF4	EC94	6BN5	EL85, N155
6AF7G	64ME*, EM34*	6BQ5	6P15, EL84, E84L, N709
6AG5	EF96	6BQ6GT	6G-B6
6AG7	6L10, OSW2192, OSW2601	6BQ7A	ECC180
6AH6	6F36	6BR3	EY88*
6AJ4	EC84	6BR5	65ME, EM80, EM81
6AJ5	6F35	6BR7	8D5
6AJ7	6F10, OSW2190, OSW2600	6BS7	8D7
6AJ8	6C12, 20D4, ECH81, X719	6BS8	6R-HH2
6AK5	6F32, DP61, E95F, EF95§, EF905, M8100§, PM05§	6BT4	66KU, EZ40, U150, U718*, UU9*, V61
6AK7	6L10, OSW2192, OSW2601	6BT6	6BC32, DH77, EBC90, EBC91
6AK8	6LD12, DH719, EABC80	6BW7	6F23, 8D6, EF80
6AL3	EY88	6BX4	EZ91*
6AL5	6B32, 6D2, D2M9, D77, D152, D717, DD6, EAA91, EB91, EAA901, EAA901S	6BX6	8D6, 64SPT, EF80, Z152, Z719
		6BX8	6R-HH2, ECC180
		6BY6	6H31, EH90, EK90
6AM5	6P17, 7D9, 16A, DD7, DDR7, EL91, M8082*	6BY7	6F19, 6F26, EF85, W719
		6C4	EC90, L77, M8080, QA2401, QL77
6AM6	6F12, 8D3, EF91, HP6, M8083, PM07, QA2403, QZ77, R144, S6F12, SP6, Z77	6C5	L63, OSW3112
		6CA4	EZ81, U709, UU12
		6CA7	7D11, 12E13, EL34, KT77, KT88
6AN7	ECH80		
6AQ4	6L34, EC91, M8099	6CB6	EF190
6AQ5	6L31, BPM04, EL90, M8245, N727	6CD7	64ME, EM34
		6CE5	EF96

§ May not work in all circuits.   * Parallel-filament circuits.

Tube Type	Replacement	Tube Type	Replacement
6CF6	EF190	6ET6	EF97, EF98
6CH6	7D10, EF82, EL821, EL822	6F5GT	H63
6CJ5	6C15, 6F16, 7F16, 62VP, EF41, HF61, W150	6F6G	KT63
		6FC7	ECC89
6CJ6	EL81, EL820	6FD6	EF97, EF98
6CK5	67PT, BF61, EL41, N150	6FG6	EM84, EM840
6CK6	EL83, EL820, EL803§	6FW8	6R-HH8, ECC88*, ECC189*
6CL6	6L43	6FY5	EC95*, EC97
6CM4	EC86, E86C*, EC806S*	6GA8	6/30L2, B729, ECC804
6CM5	6G-B7, EL36, EL360	6GB5	EL500
6CN6	5P29, EL38	6GJ7	ECF801
6CQ6	6F21, 9D6, EF92, M8161, QA2400, QW77, V177, V884, VP6, W77	6GM8	ECC86
		6GV7	6C18, ECF805
		6GV8	ECL85
6CS6	6H31, EH90, EK90	6GW8	ECL86
6CT7	D61§, EAF42, WD150	6GX8	EAM86
6CU6	6G-B9	6H5G	6M1
6CU7	62TH, ECH42, ECH43, ECH113, 6C9*, 6C10*, X150*	6H6	D63, EB34*, OSW3109
		6HA5	EC900
		6HC8	ECL82*
6CV7	6LD3, 62DDT, DH150, DH718, EBC41	6HG5	6L31, 6P9, EL90, N727
		6HG8	ECF86
6CW5	EL86	6HL8	6C16, ECF80
6CW7	6L16, ECC84	6HM5	EC900
6D4	EN93	6HQ5	EC900
6D8	X73*, X73M*	6HQ6	EF190
6DA5	65ME, EM80, EM81	6HU6	EM87
6DA6	EF89	6HU8	ELL80
6DC6	EF190	6J4	6M-H1, M8232, TM12
6DC8	6FD12, EBF85, EBF89	6J5	L63, L63B, OSW3112
6DG7	EF89F	6J6	6CC31, 6M-HH3, ECC91, M8081, T2M05
6DJ8	ECC88, ECC189, E88CC*		
6DL4	EC88	6J7	A863, EF37*, Z63
6DL5	EL95	6J7GT	A863, KTW63, KTZ63, KTZ63M, Z63, EF37*
6DQ6A	6G-B9		
6DR6	EL81, EL820	6JW8	ECF802
6DR8	EBF83	6JX8	ECH84
6DS8	ECH83	6K7	PF9, W61, W63, EF39*, OM6*, W147*
6DT8	6AT7N		
6DX8	ECL84	6KH8	ECLL8001
6DY5	EL82	6KN8	6R-HH8, ECC88*, ECC189*
6E5	6S5G, OSW3110	6L6	EL37
6E8G	X61M, X147, ECH35*, TH62*	6L6GC	KT66
6EB5	6B32, 6D2, D2M9, D77, D152, D717, DD6, EAA91, EB91, EAA901, EAA901S	6L7	X64
		6LN8	LCF80
		6LX8	LCF802
		6M5	EL80
6EC4	EY500	6M6G	EL33*, KT61*, N147*, PP6BG§
6EC7	6F18, W739		
6EH7	6F25, 6F29, EF183, EF811	6N3	EY80, EY82
6EJ7	6F24, 6F30, EF184, EF814	6N8	EBF80, EBF81, WD709, ZD152
6EL7	6F23, EF812, Z749		
6ER5	EC95, EC97*	6Q4	EC80
6ES6	EF97, EF98	6Q7	DH63
6ES8	ECC88, ECC189		

Tube Type	Replacement	Tube Type	Replacement
6R3	63VP*, EY81, EY83*, EY88*	8HG8	PCF86
6R4	EC81	8U9	PCF201
6R8	6LD12, DH719, EABC80	8X9	PCF200
6S2	EY86, EY87	9A8	30C1, LZ319, LZ329, PCF80
6S2A	EY87	9AK8	PABC80
6S7	OF1, OM5*	9AQ8	PCC85
6SA7	OSW3104	9BM5	9P9
6SK7	OSW3111	9EA8	30C1, LZ319, LZ329,
6SL7	ECC35*		PCF80, PCF82
6SN7GT	13D2, B65, ECC32*,	9EN7	30C15, LZ339, PCF800
	QA2408, QB65	9GB8	30FL1, PCE800
6SQ7	OSW3105	9GV8	XCL85
6T8	6LD12, DH719, EABC80	9JW8	PCF802
6U3	EY80	9U8	30C1, LZ319, LZ329,
6U8	ECF80, ECF82		PCF80, PCF82
6U9	ECF201	9V9	PCH200
6V3	EY81F	10CW5	LL86
6V4	EZ80	10DE7	9R-AL1
6V6GT	OSW3106*	10DX8	LCL84
6V9	ECH200	10GV8	LCL85
6W7G	8D4*	11BM8	LCL82
6X2	EY51, R12, SU61, U43,	11R3	LY81
	U45, U151	11Y9	LFL200
6X4	6Z31, E90Z, EZ90, EZ900,	12A8	OH4
	U707, V2M70, QA2407*,	12AC5	10F9, 121VP, HF121, UF41,
	U78*		W118, W142, W145
6X5G	EZ35, U147, U70*	12AD7	6L13*
6X9	ECF200	12AF3	12R-K19
6Y9	EFL200	12AH8	20D3
6Z3	AD	12AJ7	HCH81
7A7	W81, W148, EF22*, W143*	12AL5	10D2, HAA91, UB91
7AN7	30L1, 30L15, B319, PCC84	12AT6	12BC32, HBC90, HBC91
7AU7	PCC186, XCC82	12AT7	B152, B309, B739, ECC81,
7B5	EL22, KT81, N148		ECC801, ECC801S, E81CC,
7B6	DH81, DL82		M8162, QA2406, QB309
7B7	W149	12AU6	12F31, HF93, HF94
7C5	EL22, KT81, N148	12AU7	B329, B749, E82CC, ECC82,
7C6	DH149		ECC186, ECC802,
7DJ8	PCC88, PCC189		ECC802S, M8136
7ED7	30F5, Z329	12AV6	12BC32, HBC90, HBC91
7EK7	30L15, B349, PCC805	12AV7	12R-LL3§
7ES8	PCC88, PCC189	12AX7	6L13, B339, B759, E83CC,
7FC7	PCC84, PCC89		ECC83, ECC803, M8137
7GV7	30C18, PCF805	12BA6	12F31, HF93, HF94
7H7	EF22*, W143*, W148	12BE6	12H31, HK90
7S7	X81, X148	12BK6	12BC32, HBC90, HBC91
7Y4	U82*, U149	12BQ6GT	12G-B6
8A8	30C1, LZ319, LZ329, PCF80,	12BR3	12R-K19
	PCF82	12BT6	12BC32, HBC90, HBC91
8B8	8R-HP1, XCL82	12BX6	10F18*, W119*
8BQ5	XL84	12BY7	EL180
8CW5	XL86	12C8	VP12D
8GJ7	PCF801, PCF806	12CS6	12H31, HK90

§ May not work in all circuits.   * Parallel-filament circuits.

Tube Type	Replacement	Tube Type	Replacement
12DF7	6L13, B339, B759, ECC83, ECC803	19X3	19BD, 19U3, 19W3, PY80, U152, U309
12DT7	6L13, B339, B759, ECC83, ECC803	19Y3	19SU, PY82, U154, U192, U319
12FB5	30P12	20AQ3	LY88
12FG6	UM84	21A6	213PEN, N152, N339, N359, PL81, PL820
12HU8	PLL80	25BQ6GT	25G-B6
12K7	W76	25E5	30P4, 30P19, N308, PL36
12K7GT	OF5, W76	20GF6	30P4, 30P19, N389, PL302
12K8	X71M, X76M	21KQ6	LL521
12Q7GT	DH74, DH76, DL74M	25A6	KT33
12S7	UAF42§, WD142§	25L6	KT32
12SN7GT	13D2, B36	25W6GT	KT32
12SQ7	OBC3	25Y4	PY31, U31
12SX7GT	B36	25Z4GT	U31
12X4	HZ90	27GB5	PL500
12Z3	HZ90	27KG6	LL505
13CM5	12G-B7, XL36	28EC4	LY500
13EC7	10F18, W110, W119	28GB5	PL500
13GB5	12B-B14, XL500	30A5	HL94
13GC8	30PL1, 30PL10, LN319	30AE3	PY88
14G6	10LD13, DH119, UBC81	31A3	311SU, U118, U142, U145, U404, UY41, UY42, V311, V312
14GW8	PCL86		
14K7	141TH, UCH42, UCH43, X142	35C5	HL94
14L7	10LD3, 141DDT, DH118, DH142, UBC41	35W4	HY90
		35Z4GT	U74, U76
14Z3	HZ90	38A3	U119, U381, UY85
15A6	N153, N309, PL83	40KG6	PL509
15CW5	30P18, N379, PL84	42EC4	PY500
15DQ8	PCL84	45A5	10P14, 451PT, BF451, N142, UL41, UL46
16A5	30P16, 30P18, 163PEN, N154, N329, N379, PL82, PL84	45B5	10P18, N119, UL84
		50BM8	10PL12, 48A8, LN119, UCL82
16A8	30PL12, N369, PCL82	50C5	HL92
16AQ3	XY88	50L6GT	KT71
16GK8	30PL13, 30PL14, PCL88, PCL800	55N3	UY82
		807	4Y25, 5S1, P17A, QE06/50, QV05-25
16Y9	PFL200		
17C8	17N8, 171DDP, UBF80	954	E1F, UN954, ZA2*
17EW8	HCC85	955	1650, 4671, E1C, HA2, UN955
17N8	UBF80		
17Z3	A61, PY81, PY83, PY800, PY801, U153, U193, U251, U349	956	E2F
		957	D1C
		958A	D2C
18FW6	19M-R9	959	D3F
18FX6	X107§	1267	Z300T
18GD6	19M-R9	2050	EN32, ME1501
18GV8	PCL85	5591	DP61, E95F, EF95, EF905, M8180
19AQ5	HL90		
19C8	HABC80	5608	DP61, E95F, EF95, EF905, M8100, M8180
19CS4	U191, U339		
19D8	10C14, 19AJ8, UCH81, X119	5624	E82M
19KF6	N22LL		
19T8	HABC80		

Tube Type	Replacement	Tube Type	Replacement
5634	EN70, ME1500	5931	U52, GZ31
5636	EF730	5932	KT66
5641	EY70	5993	6Z31, EZ90, M8138,
5642	DY70		QA2407, QU78, U78,
5643	EN70		U707, V2M70
5647	EA71	6004	U50
5651	85A2, M8098, OG3,	6005	M8245
	STV85/10	6007	DL67
5654	DP61, E95F, EF95, EF905,	6008	DF67
	M8100, M8180, PM05	6024	6F12, 8D3, EF91, HP6,
5660	VP12D		M8083, PM07, QA2403,
5672	DL69, DL75, DL620, DL652,		QZ77, SP6, Z77
	XFY14	6030	ECC91, M8081, T2M05
5676	XFR3	6042	13D1
5678	DF60, DF654, XFR2	6050	XFR3
5696	EN92	6057	B339, B759, ECC83,
5718	EC70		ECC803, M8137
5725	M8196	6058	6D2, D77, D152, D717,
5726	6D2, D2M9, D77, D152,		D2M9, DD6, DD6G,
	D717, DD6, DD6G,		EAA91, EB91, QA2404,
	E91AA, EAA91, EAA901S,		QD77
	EB91, M8079, M8212,	6059	8D5
	QA2404, QD77	6060	ECC801
5727	M8204, E91N, EN91, PL21	6062	M8096
5731	E1F, ZA2	6063	6Z31, EZ90, EZ90Z, EZ900,
5749	EF93, M8101, PM04, W727		M8138, QA2407, QU78,
5750	EK90, MH04, X77, X727		U78, U707, V2M70
5751	B759, ECC83, B339, M8137	6064	6F12, 8D3, EF91, HP6,
5757	E91N, EN91, M8204, PL21		M8083, PM07, QA2403,
5763	QE03/10, QV03-12		QZ77, SP6, Z77
5783	85A3, M8190	6065	6F21, 9D6, EF92, M8161,
5802	ME1401		QA2400, QW77, VP6, W77
5814	B749, M8136	6067	B749, M8136
5823	Z900T	6073	150C2, 150C4, HD51,
5838	EZ35, U70, U147		M8223, STV150/30
5840	EF732	6074	180C1, HD52, M8224,
5847	6R-R8, 6R-R8C, E182F		STV108/30
5852	EZ35, U70, U147	6080	7D11, 12E13, A1834,
5861	EC55		ECC230, EL34, KT88
5881	EL37, KT66	6084	E80F
5886	DF703	6085	E80CC
5889	ME1403	6086	18042, TS53
5894	QQC04/15, QQE06/40,	6087	U50
	QQV06-40	6096	DP61, E95F, EF95, EF905,
5899	EF731		M8100, M8180, PM05
5900	EF71	6097	D717, M8212
5901	EF72, EF732, M8121	6099	ECC91, M8081, T2M05
5902	EL71	6100	EC90, L77, M8080,
5910	DF904		QA2401, QL77
5911	DF67	6101	ECC91, M8081, T2M05
5913	DL67	6105	U50
5915	E91H, EH900S	6106	ECC91, M8081, T2M05
5920	E90C, E90CC		

§ May not work in all circuits.   * Parallel-filament circuits.

Tube Type	Replacement	Tube Type	Replacement
6125	EC90, L77, M8080, QA2401, QL77	6679	B739
		6680	B749
6132	7D10, EF82, EL821, EL822, M8135	6681	B339, B759, E83CC, ECC83, M8137
6135	EC90, L77, M8080, QA2401, QL77	6686	E81L
		6687	E91H
6136	EF94	6688	E180F
6146	QE05/40, QV06-20	6689	E83F
6157	R17	6778	EC70
6158	13D3	6779	Z803U
6159	QE05/40H	6922	E88CC
6186	EF96	6923	EA52
6189	B749, E82CC, ECC802, M8136	6939	QQE02/5, QQV02-6
		6977	DM160
6195	DL700	7001	M8167
6201	E81CC, ECC801S, M8162	7025	B339, B759, ECC83, M8137
6202	6Z31, EZ90, M8138, QA2407, QU78, U78, U707, V2M70	7027	KT66
		7027A	KT88
		7062	E180CC
6203	6Z31, EZ90, M8138, QA2407, QU78, U78, U707, V2M70	7118	E181CC
		7119	E182CC
		7247	B759
6205	EF734	7292	JN2-25W
6218	E80T	7308	E188CC
6227	E80L	7316	ECC186
6252	QQE03/20, QQV03-20	7320	E84L
6267	8D8, 6F22, EF86, EF87, EF806S, M8195, Z729	7378	QE08/200, QV08-100
		7408	OSW3106
6281	CK512AX	7534	E180L
6351	Z319	7543	EF94
6354	150B2, M8163	7581	KT66, KT77
6360	QQE03/12, QQV03-10	7643	E80CF
6370	E1T	7693	E90F
6373	DL70	7694	E99F
6374	EY84	7709	Z70W
6375	DC70	7710	Z70U
6391	EF74	7711	Z71U
6443	EY84, M8091, R18	7713	Z804U
6463	CC86E, ECC86, ECC813	7714	Z805U
6487	EF70, M8125	7722	E280F
6488	EF73, M8122	7737	E186F
6489	EA76, M8123	7788	E810F
6516	M8082	8101	EC157
6535	ECC91, M8081, T2M05	8223	E288CC
6550	7D11, 12E13, KT88	8228	ZZ1000
6574	EN32, ME1501	8233	E55L
6611	DF61	8254	EC1000
6626	150C2, 150C4, HD51, M8223, STV150/30	8255	E88C, EC88
		8278	EL503, F1EL
6627	108C1, HD52, M8224, STV108/30	8453	Z550M
		9905	QQC04/15
6660	EF93, M8101, PM04, W727	9910	QQE03/20, QQV03-20

American Substitutes for Foreign Types

This section lists American substitutes for foreign tubes. Foreign tubes are shown in the left-hand column; American equivalents are in the right-hand column. Only those foreign types which can be replaced with American brands have been listed. For a list of foreign equivalents for American types, refer to Section 5.

In most cases, there is only one American replacement shown as a direct equivalent to the foreign type. Other equivalents for the American replacement are listed in Sections 1, 3, and 4. For example, the American replacement for the 6F10 is the 6AC7. If a 6AC7 is not available, Section 1 shows that a 6AJ7 can be used as a substitute. Therefore, the 6AJ7 can be used as a substitute for the 6F10.

Substitutes marked with an asterisk (*) should be used only when the filament of the original tube is wired in a parallel circuit. Those tubes marked with a section symbol (§) may not work in all circuits.

Tube Type	Replacement	Tube Type	Replacement	Tube Type	Replacement
1C1	1R5	6D-HH13	6FX7	6T1	6AF4
1C2	1AC6	6F10	6AC7	6V3P	6R3*
1C3	1AB6	6F11	6AM6	6V4	6CA4
1D13	1A3	6F12	6AM6	6Z4	6BX4
1F1	1AJ4	6F15	6CJ5	6Z31	6X4
1F2	1L4	6F16	6CJ5	7D9	6AM5
1F3	1T4	6F18	6EC7	7D10	6CH6
1FD1	1AH5	6F19	6BY7	7D11	6550
1FD9	1S5	6F21	6CQ6	7F16	6CJ5
1G50	2050A	6F22	6267	8D3	6AM6
1H2	1S2	6F23	6EL7	8D4	6W7G*
1H33	1AQ5, 1R5SF, 1R5*	6F24	6EJ7	8D5	6BR7
1H35	1AB6	6F25	6EH7	8D6	6BW7
1M1	1N3	6F26	6BY7	8D7	6BS7
1P1	3C4	6F29	6EH7	8D8	6269
1P10	3S4	6F30	6EJ7	8R-HP1	8B8
1P11	3V4	6F31	6BA6	9D6	6CQ6
1RK23	1S2	6F32	6AK5	9P9	9BM5
1S5SF	1AR5	6F33	6AS6	9R-AL1	10DE7
1U5SF	1AS5	6F35	6AJ5	9R-HH2	9GH8A
2B/250A	807	6F36	6AH6	9RHR2	9GH8
3M-R24	3DK6	6FD12	6DC8	10C14	19D8
3M-V7	3BZ6	6FX4	6AV4*	10F9	12AC5
3S4SF	3W4	6G-B3A	6BQ6GT	10F18	13EC7
4G280K	2D21	6G-B6	6DQ6A	10LD3	14L7
4R-HH2	4BS8	6G-B9	6GW6	10LD13	14G6
4R-HH8	4KN8	6G-K17	6AU4GT	10P18	45B5
4Y25	807	6H31	6BE6	10PL12	50BM8
5A/160H	6AM6	6L10	6AG7	12B-B14	13GB5
5B/250A	807	6L12	6AQ8	12BC32	6550
5M-HH3	5J6	6L13	12AX7	12E13	12BA6
5P29	6CN6	6L16	6CW7	12F31	12GW6
5R-HP1	4BL8	6L31	6AQ5	12G-B3	12BQ6GT
5S1	807	6L34	6AQ4	12G-B6	12AV6
5Z10	5U4G	6L43	6CL6	12G-B7	13CM5
6/30L2	6GA8	6LD3	6CV7	12G-K17	12D4A
6AT7N	6DT8	6LD12	6AK8	12H31	12BE6
6B32	6AL5	6LD13	6BD7	12R-K19	12BR3
6BC32	6AV6	6LP12	6BM8	12R-LL3	12AV7
6C9	6CU7*	6M1	6U5G	12R-LL5	12FQ7
6C10	6CU7*	6M2	6CD7	13D2	6SN7GT
6C12	6AJ8	6M-H1	6J4	13D3	6158
6C15	6CJ5	6M-HH3	6J6	16A	6AM5
6C16	6BL8	6P9	6BM5	17N8	17C8
6C18	6GV7	6P15	6BQ5	18AK5	6028
6C31	6K8	6P17	6AM5	19AJ8	19D8
6CC10	5692	6P25	6AG6	19BD	19X3
6CC31	6J6	6PL12	6BM8	19M-R9	18GD6
6CC42	5670	6Q8	6A8	19M-R10	18GD6
6CC43	6AQ8	6R-HH2	6BS8	19SU	19Y3
6CF8	6267	6R-HH8	6KN8	19U3	19X3
6CH40	6AJ8	6R-K19	6AV3	19W3	19X3
6D1	2B35	6R-R8C	5847	20A3	2D21
6D2	6AL5	6S5G	6E5	20D3	12AH8

Tube Type	Replacement	Tube Type	Replacement	Tube Type	Replacement
20D4	6AJ8	A2521	6CR4	DCC90	3A5
25G-B6	25BQ6GT	A2900	12AT7	DCF60	1V6
25R-K19	25BR3	AA91E	5726	DD6	6AL5
30C1	9A8	ABC91	12A6	DD7	6AM5
30C15	9EN7	AD	6Z3	DD77	5726
30C18	7GV7	AG5211	0A2	DDR7	6AM5
30F5	7ED7	ARS25A	807	DF26	1S5
30FL1	9GB8	ASG512	2D21	DF33	1N5GT
30L1	7AN7	ATS225A	807	DF60	5678
30L15	7EK7	B36	12SN7GT	DF62	1AD4
30P4	25GF6	B63	6A6	DF67	5911, 6008
30P12	12FB5	B65	6SN7GT	DF91	1T4
30P16	16A5	B139	7AN7	DF92	1L4
30P18	15CW5	B152	12AT7	DF96	1AJ4
30P19	25GF6	B309	12AT7	DF97	1AN5
30PL1	13GC8	B319	7AN7	DF652	1AD4
30PL10	13GC8	B329	12AU7	DF668	1AD4
30PL12	16A8	B339	12AX7	DF904	1U4
30PL13	16GK8	B349	7EK7	DH63	6Q7
30PL14	16GK8	B719	6AQ8	DH74	12Q7GT
40SUA	1D5	B729	6GA8	DH76	12Q7GT
52KU	5Z4G	B739	12AT7	DH77	6AT6
54KU	5AQ4	B749	12AU7	DH81	7B6
62DDT	6CV7	B759	12AX7	DH118	14L7
62TH	6CU7	BA2	2050	DH119	14G6
62VP	6CJ5	BF61	6CK5	DH142	14L7
63TP	6AB8	BF451	45A5	DH149	7C6
64ME	6CD7	BPM04	6AQ5	DH150	6CV7
64SPT	6BX6	BVA264	6AG6G	DH718	6CV7
65ME	6BR5	BVA265	6AG6G	DH719	6AK8
66KU	6BT4	C610	7J7	DH817	6CV7
67PT	6CK5	CC81E	12AT7WA	DK32	1A7GT
85A1	0E3	CC86E	6GM8	DK91	1R5
85A2	0G3	CSF80	4BL8	DK92	1AC6
85A3	5783	D1C	957	DK96	1AB6
108C1	0B2	D2C	958A	DK97	1AB6
121VP	12AC5	D2M9	6AL5	DL29	3D6
141DDT	14L7	D3F	959	DL31	1A5G
141TH	14K7	D61	6CT7§	DL33	3Q5GT
150B2	6354	D63	6H6	DL35	1C5GT
150C1	0A2	D77	6AL5	DL36	1Q5GT
150C2	0A2	D152	6AL5	DL37	6L6GC
150C3	0D3	D717	6AL5	DL67	5913, 6007
150C4	0A2	DA90	1A3	Dl74M	12Q7
163PEN	16A5	DAC21	1S5	DL82	7B6
171DDP	17C8	DAC32	1H5GT	DL91	1S4
213PEN	21A6	DAF90	1A3	DL92	3S4
311SU	31A3	DAF91	1S5	DL93	3A4
451PT	45A5	DAF92	1U5	DL94	3V4
A61	17Z3	DAF96	1AH5	DL95	3Q4
A677	6C6	DAF97	1AN5	DL96	3C4
A863	6J7GT	DC70	6375	DL98	3B4
A1834	6AS7G	DC80	1E3	DL620	5672

§ May not work in all circuits.   * Parallel-filament circuits.

Tube Type	Replacement	Tube Type	Replacement	Tube Type	Replacement
DM70	1M3	EA41	6CT7	ECC91	6J6
DM71	1N3	EA50	2B35	ECC180	6BQ7A
DM160	6977	EA76	6489	ECC186	12AU7
DP61	6AK5	EAA91	6AL5	ECC189	6ES8
DY30	1B3GT	EAA901	5726	ECC230	6080
DY51	1BG2	EABC80	6AK8	ECC801	6060
DY70	5642	EAF41	6CT7§	ECC802	6189
DY80	1X2A	EAF42	6CT7	ECC803	6057
DY86	1S2	EAM86	6GX8	ECC804	6GA8
DY87	1S2A	EB34	6H6*	ECC808	6KX8
DY802	1BQ2	EB91	6AL5	ECC813	6463
E1F	954	EBC3	6BD7A	ECC863	12DT7
E2F	956	EBC41	6CV7	ECC900	6HA5
E55L	8233	EBC80	6BD7	ECF80	6BL8
E80CC	6085	EBC81	6BD7	ECF82	6U8
E80CF	7643	EBC90	6AT6	ECF86	6HG8
E80F	6084	EBC91	6AV6	ECF200	6X9
E80L	6227	EBF32	6B8*	ECF201	6U9
E80T	6218	EBF41	6CJ5	ECF202	6AJ9
E81CC	12AT7, 6201	EBF80	6N8	ECF801	6GJ7
E81L	6686	EBF81	6AD8	ECF802	6JW8
E82CC	12AU7	EBF83	6DR8	ECF805	6GV7
E83CC	6681	EBF85	6DC8	ECH35	6E8G*
E83F	6689	EBF89	6DC8	ECH42	6CU7
E84L	7320	EC22	6R4	ECH80	6AN7
E88C	6DL4, 8255	EC55	5861	ECH81	6AJ8
E88CC	6922	EC70	5718	ECH82	6E8
E89F	6DG7	EC71	5718	ECH83	6DS8
E90C	5920	EC80	6Q4	ECH84	6JX8
E90CC	5920	EC81	6R4	ECH113	6CU7
E90F	6BH6	EC84	6AJ4	ECH200	6V9
E90Z	6X4	EC86	6CM4	ECL80	6AB8
E91AA	5726	EC88	6DL4, 8255	ECL82	6BM8
E91H	6687	EC90	6C4	ECL84	6DX8
E91N	5727	EC91	6AQ4	ECL85	6GV8
E95F	6AK5	EC92	6AB4	ECL86	6GW8
E99F	6BJ6	EC93	6BS4	ECL100	6BZ7
E130L	7534	EC94	6AF4	ECL821	6CH6
E180F	6688	EC95	6ER5	ECLL800	6KH8
E180CC	7062	EC97	6FY5	ED2	6AL5
E180L	7534	EC806S	6CM4*	ED500	6ED4
E182CC	7119	EC900	6HA5	EF13	6DA6
E182F	5847	EC1000	8254	EF22	7A7*
E186F	7737	ECC32	6SN7GT	EF36	6J7
E188CC	7308	ECC35	6SL7*	EF37	6J7GT*
E280F	7722	ECC70	6021	EF39	6K7*
E288CC	8223	ECC81	12AT7	EF41	6CJ5
E810F	7788	ECC82	12AU7	EF70	6487
E902	6X4	ECC83	12AX7	EF71	5899
E1485	3A4	ECC84	6CW7	EF72	5840
E2016	6CQ6	ECC85	6AQ8	EF73	6488
E2157	12AT7	ECC86	6GM8	EF74	6391
E2163	12AU7	ECC88	6DJ8	EF80	6BX6
E2164	12AX7	ECC89	6FC7	EF81	6BH5

Tube Type	Replacement	Tube Type	Replacement	Tube Type	Replacement
EF82	6CH6	EL509	6KG6A	GZ34	5AR4
EF83	6BK8	EL802	6LD6	GZ37	5AR4
EF85	6BY7	EL803	6CK6§	H52	5U4GB
EF86	6267	EL820	6CK6	H63	6F5GT
EF87	6267	EL821	6CH6	H2-10	2X2A
EF89	6DA6	EL822	6CH6	HAA91	12AL5
EF89F	6DG7	ELF86	6HG8	HABC80	19T8
EF91	6AM6	ELL80	6HU8	HBC90	12AT6
EF92	6CQ6	EM34	6CD7	HBC91	12AV6
EF93	6BA6	EM35	6U5	HCC85	17EW8
EF94	6AU6	EM80	6BR5	HCH81	12AJ7
EF95	6AK5	EM81	6DA5	HD14	1H5GT
EF96	6AG5	EM84	6FG6	HD30	3B4
EF97	6ES6	EM85	6DG7	HD51	0A2
EF98	6ET6	EM87	6HU6	HD52	0B2
EF183	6EH7	EM840	6FG6	HD93	1X2B
EF184	6EJ7	EN32	2050	HD94	6BQ6GTB
EF190	6CB6	EN91	2D21	HD96	25BQ6GTB
EF730	5636	EN93	6D4	HF61	6CJ5
EF731	5899	EQ80	6BE7	HF93	12BA6
EF732	5840, 5901	EY51	6X2	HF94	12AU6
EF734	6205	EY80	6U3	HF121	12AC5
EF811	6EH7	EY81	6R3	HK90	12BE6
EF812	6EL7	EY81F	6V3	HL86	30CW5
EF814	6EJ7	EY82	6N3	HL90	19AQ5
EF905	5654	EY83	6AL3*	HL92	50C5
EFL200	6Y9	EY84	6374	HL94	30A5
EH90	6CS6	EY86	6S2	HM04	6BE6
EK90	6BE6	EY87	6S2A	HP6	6AM6
EL33	6M6G*	EY88	6AL3	HY90	35W4
EL34	6CA7	EY500	6EC4	HY145	1U4
EL36	6CM5	EZ3	6V4	HZ50	14Z3
EL37	6L6	EZ4	6CA4	HZ90	12X4
EL38	6CN6	EZ11	6V4	KD21	0A3
EL41	6CK5	EZ22	7Y4	KD24	0C3
EL71	5902	EZ35	6X5G	KD25	0D3
EL80	6M5	EZ40	6BT4	KL35	1F5G*
EL81	6CJ6	EZ80	6V4	KT32	25W6GT
EL82	6DY5	EZ81	6CA4	KT33	25A6
EL83	6CK6	EZ90	6X4	KT61	6M6G*
EL84	6BQ5	EZ91	6AV4	KT63	6F6G
EL85	6BN5	EZ900	6063	KT66	6L6GC
EL86	6CW5	FA6	5677	KT71	50L6GT
EL90	6AQ5	F1EL	8278	KT77	6CA7
EL91	6AM5	G75/2D	0A3	KT88	6550
EL95	6DL5	G77	6C6	KTW63	6J7GT
EL180	12BY7	G105/1D	0C3	KTZ63	6K7GT
EL300	6FN5	G150/3D	0D3	KTZ63M	6J7GT
EL500	6GB5	G/50/4K	0A2	KY80	5J2
EL503	8278	GY501	3BH2	L63	6J5
EL504	6GB5	GZ30	5Z4G	L63B	6J5
EL505	6KG6	GZ31	5U4G	L77	6C4
EL508	6KW6	GZ32	5V4GA	LC97	3FY5

§ May not work in all circuits.   * Parallel-filament circuits.

Tube Type	Replacement	Tube Type	Replacement	Tube Type	Replacement
LC900	3HA5	N18	3Q4	PC89	7F7
LCC189	5ES8	N19	3V4	PC93	4BS4
LCF80	6LN8	N22LL	19KF6	PC95	4GK5
LCF86	5HG8	N25	3C4	PC97	4FY5
LCF200	5X9	N30EL	6LF6	PC900	4HA5
LCF201	5U9	N47	6AM5	PCC18	7AU7
LCF801	5GJ7	N63	45A5	PCC85	9AQ8
LCF802	6LX8	N66	6K6GT	PCC84	7AN7
LCH200	5V9	N77	6L6GT	PCC88	7DJ8
LCL82	11BM8	N78	6AM5	PCC89	7FC7
LCL84	10DX8	N119	6BJ5	PCC186	7AU7
LCL85	10GV8	N142	45B5	PCC189	7ES8
LCL200	10DX8	N144	6AM5	PCC805	7EK7
LF183	4EH7	N147	6M6G*	PCE800	9GB8
LF184	4EJ7	N148	7C5	PCF80	9A8
LFL200	11Y9	N150	6CK5	PCF82	9U8
LL86	10CW5	N152	21A6	PCF86	8HG8
LL500	18GB5	N153	15A6	PCF200	8X9
LL505	27KG66	N154	16A5	PCF201	8U9
LL521	21KQ6	N155	6BN5	PCF800	9EN7
LN119	50BM8	N308	25E5	PCF801	8GJ7
LN152	6AB8	N309	15A6	PCF802	9JW8
LN319	13GC8	N329	16A5	PCF805	7GV7
LY81	11R3	N359	21A6	PCF806	8GJ7
LY88	20AQ3	N369	16A8	PCH200	9V9
LY500	28EC4	N378	15CW5	PCL82	16A8
LZ319	9A8	N379	15CW5	PCL84	15DQ8
LZ329	9A8	N389	25GF6	PCL85	18GV8
LZ339	9EN7	N709	6BQ5	PCL86	14GW8
M8063	6AM6	N727	6AQ5	PCL88	16GK8
M8079	5726	OBC3	12SQ7	PCL800	16GK8
M8080	6C4	OF1	6S7	PCL801	13GC8
M8081	6J6	OF5	12K7GT	PD500	9ED4
M8096	5763	OH4	12A8	PF9	6K7
M8100	5654	OM3	6H6*	PF86	4HR8
M8101	6BA6	OM4	6R7G	PF88	7ED7
M8121	5840	OM5	6S7*	PFL200	16Y9
M8136	6189	OM6	6K7	PH4	6A8
M8137	12AX7A	OSW2190	6AC7	PL21	2D21
M8162	12AT7WA	OSW2192	6AG7	PL36	25E5
M8196	5725	OSW2600	6AC7	PL81	21A6
M8204	5727	OSW2601	6AG7	PL82	16A5
M8212	5726	OSW3104	6SA7	PL83	15A6
M8223	0A2WA	OSW3105	6SQ7	PL84	15CW5
M8224	0B2WA	OSW3106	6V6GT*	PL300	35FN5
M8232	6J4WA	OSW3107	5CG4, 5Z4G	PL302	25GF6
M8245	6AQ5, 6005	OSW3109	6H6	PL500	27GB5
MU14	6BT4	OSW3110	6E5	PL505	40KG6
MV6-5	6SA7GT	OSW3111	6SK7	PL508	17KW6
N2ED	6HT5	OSW3112	6J5	PL509	40KG6
N14	1C5GT	P17A	807	PL521	29KQ6
N15	3Q5GT	PABC80	9AK8	PL801	12FB5
N16	3Q5GT	PC86	4CM4	PL820	21A6
N17	3S4	PC88	4DL4	PL1267	0A4G

Tube Type	Replacement	Tube Type	Replacement	Tube Type	Replacement
PLL80	12HU8	QW77	6CQ6	U82	7Y4*
PM04	6BA6	QZ77	6AM6	U118	31A3
PM05	6AK5§	R3	1W4	U119	38A3
PM07	6AM6	R10	6305	U142	31A3
PM95	6AK6	R12	6X2	U145	31A3
PP6BG	6M6G§	R16	1T2	U147	6X5G
PY80	19X3	R19	1X2A	U149	7Y4
PY81	17Z3	R20	2J2	U150	6BT4
PY82	19Y3	R52	5Z4G	U151	6X2
PY83	17Z3	R144	6AM6	U152	19X3
PY88	30AE3	RJ2	5Y2	U153	17Z3
PY301	19CS4	RL21	2D21	U154	19Y3
PY500	42EC4	RL1267	0A4G	U191	19CS4
PY800	17Z3	RS2	5Z4	U192	19Y3
PY801	17Z3	RS1029	6360	U193	17Z3
QA2401	6135	S6F12	6AM6	U251	17Z3
QA2404	5726	S856	0A2	U309	19X3
QA2406	12AT7WB	S860	0B2	U319	19Y3
QA2407	6201	SM150-30	0A2	U329	25BR3
QA2408	5692	SP6	6AM6	U339	19CS4
QB65	6SN7GT	SR2	0G3	U349	17Z3
QB309	12AT7	SR3	0B2	U381	38A3
QB5/1750	6079	SR55	0B2	U707	6X4
QE03/10	5763	SR56	0A2	U709	6CA4
QE05/40	6146	STR85/10	0G3	U718	6BT4*
QE05/40H	6159	STR108/30	0A2	UAF42	12S7
QE06/50	807	STR150/30	0A2	UBC41	14L7
QL77	6C4	STV85/10	0G3	UBC80	14G6
QM556	6X4W	STV108/30	0B2	UBC81	14G6
QM557	5654	STV150/30	0A2	UBF80	17C8
QM558	5725	SU61	6X2	UBF89	19FL8
QM559	5726	T6D	2B35	UC92	9AB4
QN77	6AM5*	T2M05	6J6	UCC85	26AQ8
QQE02/5	6939	T77	6C6	UCH42	14K7
QQE03/12	6360	TH62	6E8G*	UCH80	14Y7
QQE03/20	6252	TTZ63	6J7	UCH81	19D8
QQE06/40	5894	TM12	6J4	UCL82	50BM8
QQV02-6	6939	U26	2J2	UF41	12AC5
QQV03-10	6360	U31	25Z4GT	UF80	19BX6
QQV03-20	6252	U37	1T2	UF85	19BY5
QS150/40	0D3	U41	1B3GT	UF89	12DA6
QS1205	0A3	U43	6X2	UL41	45A5
QS1206	0C3	U45	6X2*	UL84	45B5
QS1207	0A2	U49	2J2	UM80	19BR5
QS1208	0B2	U50	5Y3GT	UM84	12FG6
QS1209	5651A	U51	5W4GT	UN954	954
QS1210	0A2WA	U52	5U4G	UN955	955
QS1211	0B2WA	U54	5AR4	UQ80	12BE7
QS2404	5726	U70	6X5G*	UU5	6BT4
QS2406	12AT7WA	U74	35Z4GT	UU9	6BT4*
QV03-12	5763	U76	35Z4GT	UU12	6CA4
QV05-25	807	U77	5AR4	UY41	31A3
QV06-20	6146	U78	6X4*	UY42	31A3

§ May not work in all circuits.   * Parallel-filament circuits.

Tube Type	Replacement	Tube Type	Replacement	Tube Type	Replacement
UY82	55N3	X17	1R5	XF183	3EH7
UY85	38A3	X18	1AC6	XF184	3EJ7
UY89	38A3	X20	1AC6	XL36	13CM5
V2M70	6X4	X25	1AB6	XI84	8EQ5
V61	6BT4	X61M	6E8G	XL86	8CW5
V153	17Z3	X63	6A8	XL500	13GB5
V177	6CQ6	X64	6L7	XXA91	3AL5
V311	31A3	X65	6E8	XXB	3C6
V312	31A3	X71M	12K8	XXD	14F7
V741	6C4	X73	6D8*	XXFM	7X7
V884	6CQ6	X73M	6D8*	XY88	16AQ3
V886	6AM5	X76M	12K8GT	Y25	1M3
VP6	6CQ6	X77	6BE6	Y61	6U5
VP12D	12C8	X79	6AE8	Y64	6U5
VR150	0D3	X81	7S7	YC95	3ER5
VSM70	6X4	X107	18FX6§	YC97	3FY5
VT83	83	X119	19D8	YCC189	5ES8
W17	1T4	X142	14K7	YCF86	5HG8
W25	1AJ4	X147	6E8G	YCL84	10DX8
W61	6K7	X148	7S7	YCL180	5BQ7A
W63	6K7	X150	6C10	YF183	4EH7
W76	12K7*	X155	6BZ8	YF184	4EJ7
W77	6CQ6	X319	6351	YL84	10BQ5
W81	7A7	X719	6AJ8	YL86	10CW5
W110	13EC7	X727	6BE6	Z14	1N5GT
W118	12AC5	XAA91	3AL5	Z63	6J7
W119	13EC7	XB91	3AL5	Z77	6AM6
W142	12AC5	XC95	2ER5	Z150	6CU7
W143	7A7*	XC97	2FY5	Z152	6BX6
W145	12AC5	XC900	2HA5	Z300T	0A4G
W147	6K7*	XCC82	7AU7	Z329	7ED7
W148	7A7	XCC189	4ES8	Z550M	8453
W149	7B7	XCF80	4BL8	Z719	6BX6
W150	6CJ5	XCF82	5U8	Z729	6267
W719	6BY7	XCF86	2HR8	Z749	6EL7
W727	6BA6	XCF801	4GJ7	Z900T	5823
W739	6EC7	XCH81	3AJ8	ZA2	954*
WD142	12S7	XCL82	8B8	ZD17	1S5
WD150	6CT7	XCL85	9GV8	ZD25	1AH5
WD709	6N8	XF80	3BX6	ZD152	6N8
WT301	83	XF85	3BY7	ZZ1000	8228
X14	1A7GT	XF94	3AU6		

Tube Basing Diagrams

This section gives the basing diagrams for American receiving and picture tubes. Receiving-tube basings are listed first in numerical order. Then the picture-tube basings are given. Obtain the basing code listed in Sections 1, 2, or 4 and then refer to the applicable diagram in this section for the pin connections.

This information will serve as a valuable guide to make quick checks when a schematic is not available.

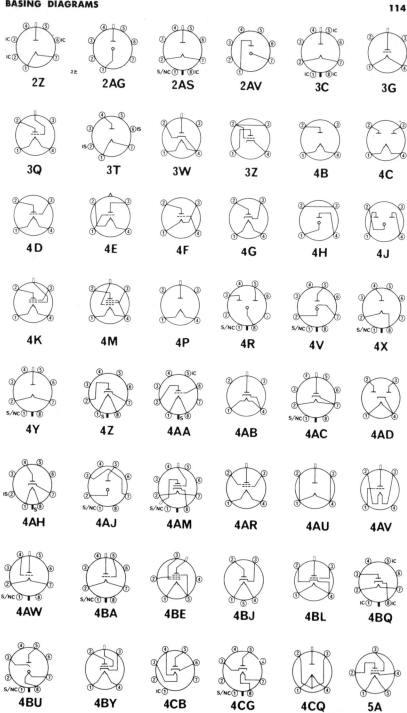

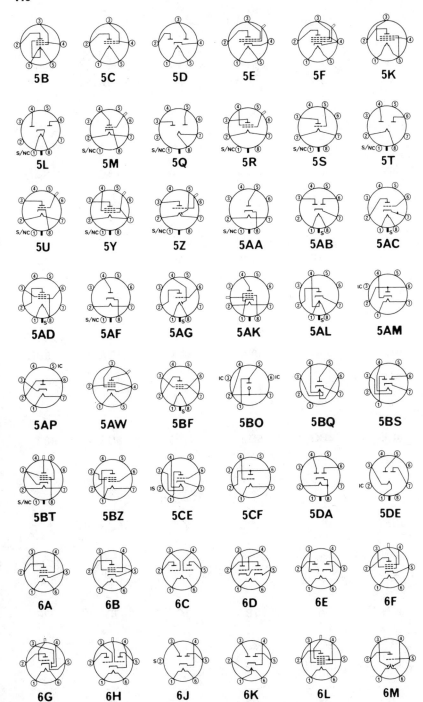

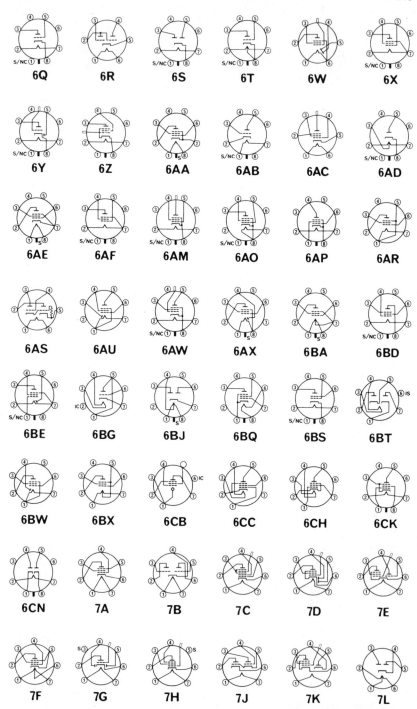

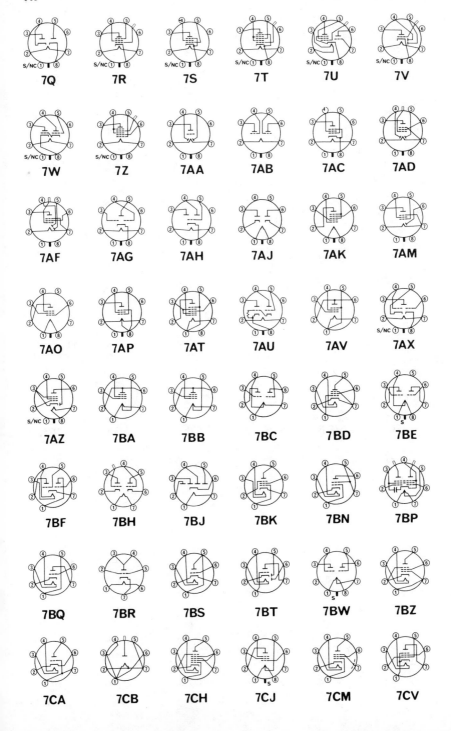

7Q 7R 7S 7T 7U 7V

7W 7Z 7AA 7AB 7AC 7AD

7AF 7AG 7AH 7AJ 7AK 7AM

7AO 7AP 7AT 7AU 7AV 7AX

7AZ 7BA 7BB 7BC 7BD 7BE

7BF 7BH 7BJ 7BK 7BN 7BP

7BQ 7BR 7BS 7BT 7BW 7BZ

7CA 7CB 7CH 7CJ 7CM 7CV

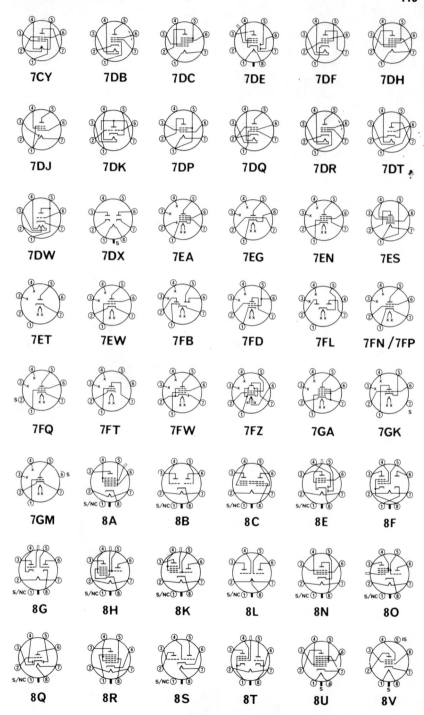

7CY 7DB 7DC 7DE 7DF 7DH

7DJ 7DK 7DP 7DQ 7DR 7DT

7DW 7DX 7EA 7EG 7EN 7ES

7ET 7EW 7FB 7FD 7FL 7FN/7FP

7FQ 7FT 7FW 7FZ 7GA 7GK

7GM 8A 8B 8C 8E 8F

8G 8H 8K 8L 8N 8O

8Q 8R 8S 8T 8U 8V

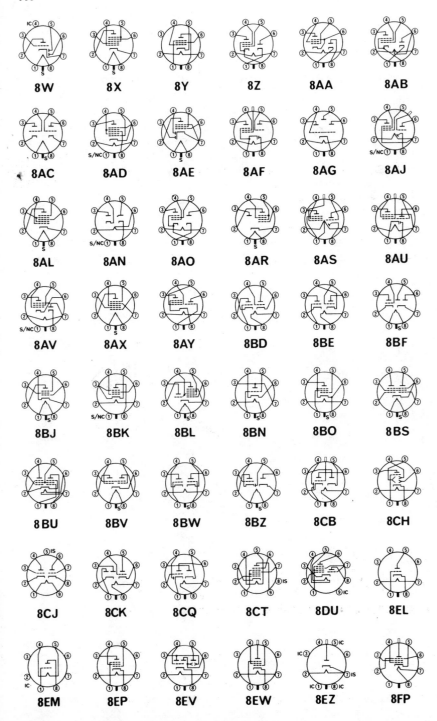

8W   8X   8Y   8Z   8AA   8AB

8AC   8AD   8AE   8AF   8AG   8AJ

8AL   8AN   8AO   8AR   8AS   8AU

8AV   8AX   8AY   8BD   8BE   8BF

8BJ   8BK   8BL   8BN   8BO   8BS

8BU   8BV   8BW   8BZ   8CB   8CH

8CJ   8CK   8CQ   8CT   8DU   8EL

8EM   8EP   8EV   8EW   8EZ   8FP

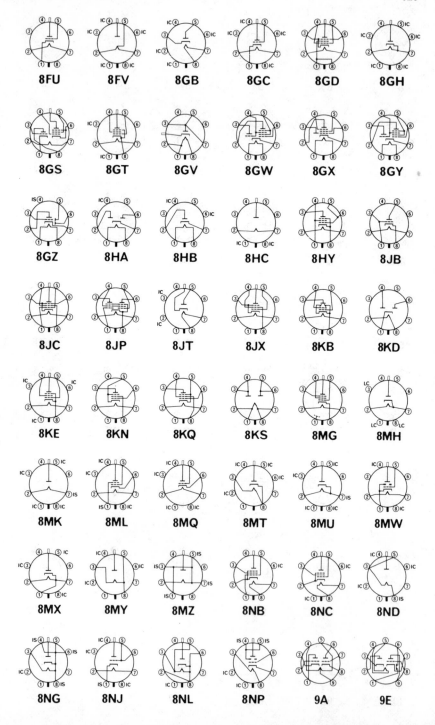

8FU 8FV 8GB 8GC 8GD 8GH

8GS 8GT 8GV 8GW 8GX 8GY

8GZ 8HA 8HB 8HC 8HY 8JB

8JC 8JP 8JT 8JX 8KB 8KD

8KE 8KN 8KQ 8KS 8MG 8MH

8MK 8ML 8MQ 8MT 8MU 8MW

8MX 8MY 8MZ 8NB 8NC 8ND

8NG 8NJ 8NL 8NP 9A 9E

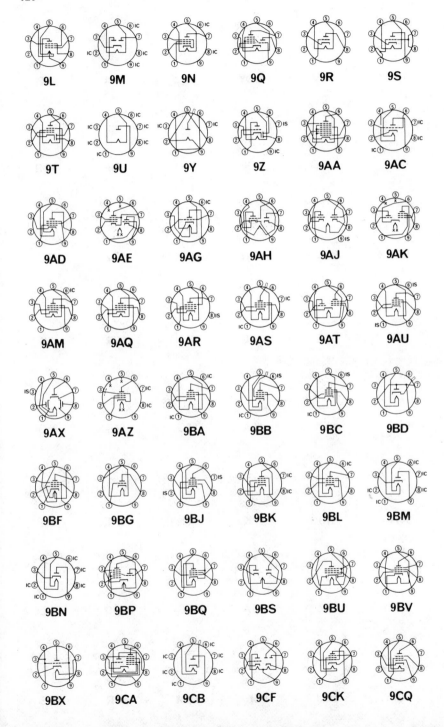

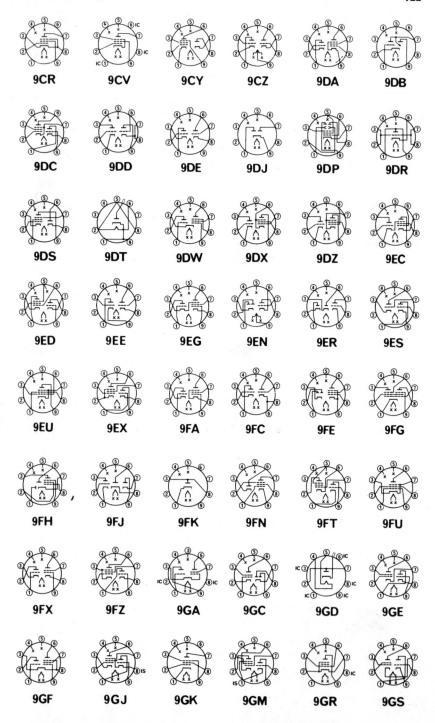

9CR 9CV 9CY 9CZ 9DA 9DB

9DC 9DD 9DE 9DJ 9DP 9DR

9DS 9DT 9DW 9DX 9DZ 9EC

9ED 9EE 9EG 9EN 9ER 9ES

9EU 9EX 9FA 9FC 9FE 9FG

9FH 9FJ 9FK 9FN 9FT 9FU

9FX 9FZ 9GA 9GC 9GD 9GE

9GF 9GJ 9GK 9GM 9GR 9GS

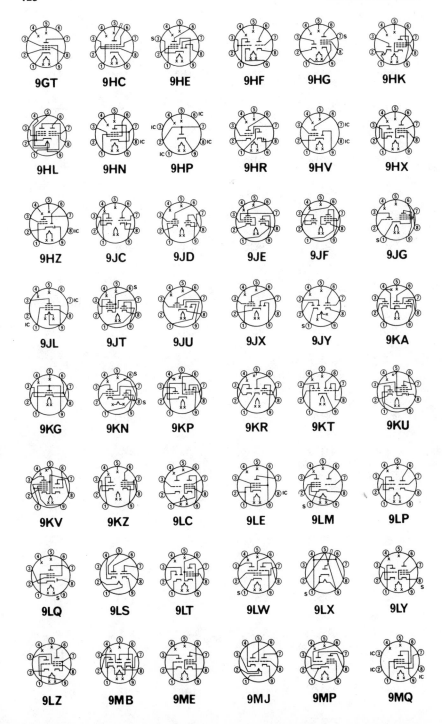

9GT 9HC 9HE 9HF 9HG 9HK

9HL 9HN 9HP 9HR 9HV 9HX

9HZ 9JC 9JD 9JE 9JF 9JG

9JL 9JT 9JU 9JX 9JY 9KA

9KG 9KN 9KP 9KR 9KT 9KU

9KV 9KZ 9LC 9LE 9LM 9LP

9LQ 9LS 9LT 9LW 9LX 9LY

9LZ 9MB 9ME 9MJ 9MP 9MQ

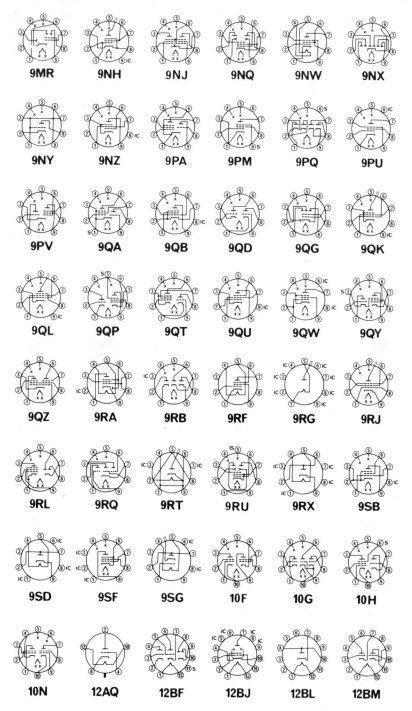

9MR   9NH   9NJ   9NQ   9NW   9NX

9NY   9NZ   9PA   9PM   9PQ   9PU

9PV   9QA   9QB   9QD   9QG   9QK

9QL   9QP   9QT   9QU   9QW   9QY

9QZ   9RA   9RB   9RF   9RG   9RJ

9RL   9RQ   9RT   9RU   9RX   9SB

9SD   9SF   9SG   10F   10G   10H

10N   12AQ   12BF   12BJ   12BL   12BM

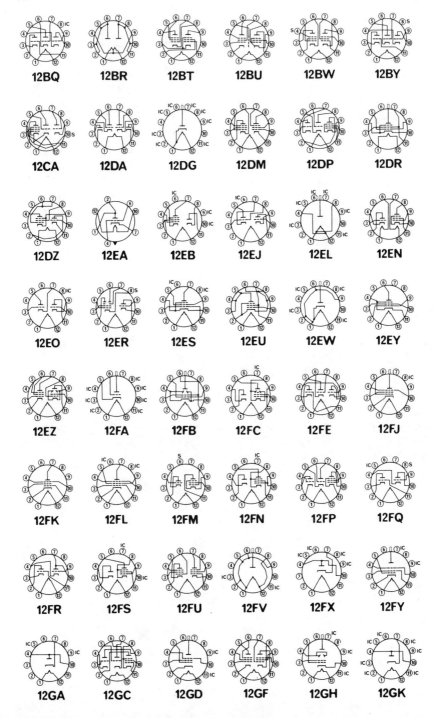

12BQ 12BR 12BT 12BU 12BW 12BY

12CA 12DA 12DG 12DM 12DP 12DR

12DZ 12EA 12EB 12EJ 12EL 12EN

12EO 12ER 12ES 12EU 12EW 12EY

12EZ 12FA 12FB 12FC 12FE 12FJ

12FK 12FL 12FM 12FN 12FP 12FQ

12FR 12FS 12FU 12FV 12FX 12FY

12GA 12GC 12GD 12GF 12GH 12GK

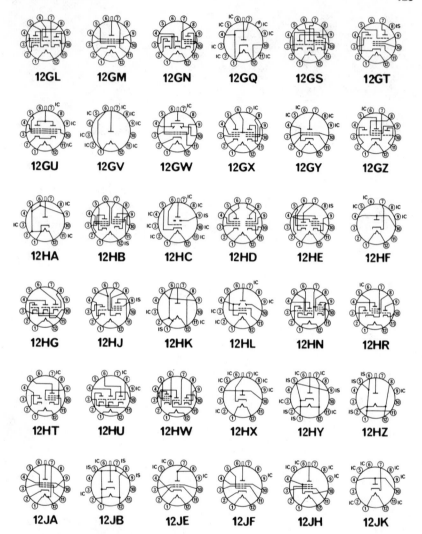

12GL 12GM 12GN 12GQ 12GS 12GT

12GU 12GV 12GW 12GX 12GY 12GZ

12HA 12HB 12HC 12HD 12HE 12HF

12HG 12HJ 12HK 12HL 12HN 12HR

12HT 12HU 12HW 12HX 12HY 12HZ

12JA 12JB 12JE 12JF 12JH 12JK

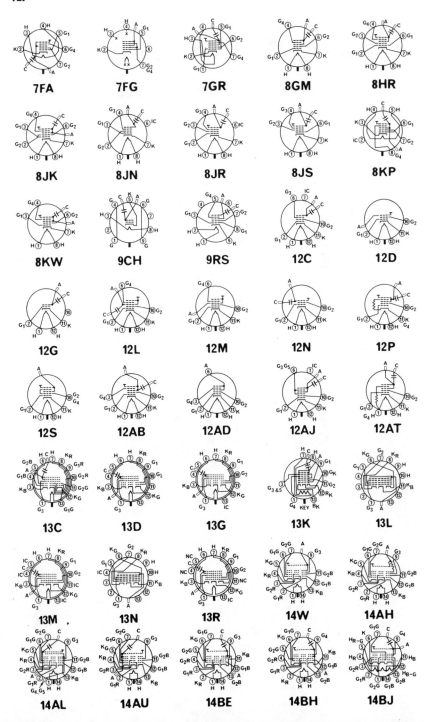

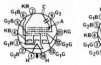

14BK **14BM** **14BP** **14BQ** **2OA**